MODERN BRITISH
MILITARY
MISSILES

PAUL BEAVER &
TERRY GANDER

All types
including E
ar

GW01003748

MODERN BRITISH
MILITARY
MISSILES

PAUL BEAVER &
TERRY GANDER

Patrick Stephens, Wellingborough

First published in 1986

British Library Cataloguing in Publication Data

Beaver, Paul
Modern British military missiles.
1. Guided missiles   2. Great Britain—
Armed Forces—Equipment
I. Title   II. Gander, Terry
623.4'51   UG1315.G7

ISBN 0-85059-837-0

*Patrick Stephens Limited is part of
Thorsons Publishing Group*

Photoset in 10 on 11 pt Helvetica Light
by Avocet Marketing Services, Bicester, Oxon.
Printed and bound in Great Britain on 115 gsm Fineblade
Cartridge for the publishers,
Patrick Stephens Limited,
Denington Estate, Wellingborough, Northants,
NN8 2QD, England.

CONTENTS

INTRODUCTION

When a decision is made to write a book on any subject one of the first things authors have to do is take an overview of the size and scope of the topic concerned. When one carries out this step in respect of guided missiles in service with the British Armed Forces the initial result is one of surprise, for there are many more missiles to cover than one would at first have thought. The range and nature of the weapons concerned is considerable, but just as wide-ranging are the life-spans of the designs concerned. Equally unexpected in many cases is their source of origin. Some have been developed within the United Kingdom, some come from the United States and others are the end results of international collaboration.

So, with the size and scope of the subject matter appreciated, it is as well to study its history to a limited extent. That is not too difficult since the history of the guided missile is not a very long one when compared to many other types of weapon. Indeed, what is now regarded as the first operational guided missile was the Brennan Torpedo deployed by the British Army to guard important harbours and waterways back in the 1880s. When the Brennans were finally replaced by coastal artillery there followed a lull in guided weapon development for some decades. During that period various far-sighted individuals, whose imaginations usually outran the technology at their disposal, constantly put forward all manner of ambitious plans for guided weapons. It was not until the 1930s that any hardware was forthcoming, however, and then only in the form of various kinds of radio-controlled aircraft.

During World War 2 the guided missile came of age with the first tentative experiments involving a variety of weapons from anti-tank to anti-aircraft missiles. The War also saw the advent of the long-range ballistic rocket (the V-2) and the first predecessor of what we now call the cruise missile (the V-1). Although the Germans were well to the fore in this early work, they were not alone. Investigations were under way in the United States and, to a lesser extent, in the United Kingdom. In both nations this work was boosted by the number of German technicians who moved to both countries in the period after May 1945 and added their considerable expertise to the work already in progress.

Some of these German technicians decided to add their knowledge to work proceeding in the United Kingdom. Much of this was already based on the mass of information captured in Germany in 1945, but not all of it came from this source. During the 1930s a great deal of know-how was gleaned from projects such as the Queen Bee radio-controlled aircraft target that provided the empirical data relating to what would be required in the future. By the end of the 1940s the way to develop guided missiles of all types was clear. On drawing boards all over the United Kingdom, aircraft manufacturers and associated companies began to formulate guided weapon designs and ideas, many of which are still in use today.

These optimistic beginnings soon ran into troubles. What was not realized at the time was that guided weapons require not just design but a great deal of development. That development required a great deal of money to match and, in the grim decade that followed the War, such money was not always forthcoming. Many promising projects simply fell by the wayside for the simple reason that there were no funds to finance them and, with their passing, many of the originating firms also passed away. The annals of the 1950s and 1960s are littered with many then-famous names that foundered on the cost of the new technology which was increasingly being bundled under the general title of 'aerospace', but missiles were not the only factor involved. Many companies were forced into some form of consortium with former rivals and others were merged as aircraft and missile projects escalated in complexity and cost. There were political considerations as well, when the Government changed from being the main paying customer into the agency that dictated policy and the degree of eventual procurement. The 1960s, especially, was an era when Government policies changed frequently and drastic prunings took with them many promising missile projects. Their very names sound down over the decades in a long sequence of what are now almost-forgotten names — Blue Steel, Blue Streak and many others.

As many United Kingdom-designed projects fell by the wayside, the military was left still requiring weapons. Increasingly the Government turned to the United States to fill the gaps, thinking — quite understandably — that a direct purchase would be much cheaper than forking out for all the design and development costs that an indigenous project would produce. Unfortunately, it did not always work out like that. The United States were no less prone to escalating costs and usually required any overseas customer to make some form of contribution to partially off-set them; the degree to which this was done often meant that buying abroad was no less expensive than buying at home. Again, a series of cancelled projects and orders littered the military procurement establishments with names like Mauler and Sky Bolt.

Out of all this confusion the current form of the British missile industry emerged with some suprisingly successful survivors of the last few decades. The British Armed Forces now have a veritable array of missile systems at their disposal but not all of them are home-produced. The Americans supply a goodly number of systems in service for the simple reason that they dominate the international missile market with some superb products. Only the United States can contemplate the vast and expensive programmes that some modern missile projects now require — Trident is a prime example. On a smaller scale, missiles like Sidewinder and Sparrow dominate the market mainly because they are not only good designs but because they are produced in such large numbers that there is no economic reason for other nations to even attempt to rival them. Having said that, there is no reason why some of them cannot be improved — the way that Sparrow has been converted into Sky Flash is yet another British success story.

Increasingly, the way ahead has been heralded not by national mergers but by international co-operation. Over the last few decades this path has been followed more and more as Europe seeks to avoid American domination of national and international markets. The results of this co-operation can be seen in the United Kingdom's missile arsenals. Systems such as Martel, Midge and Milan are already in use and MLRS is still to come.

This international flavour to the British missile scene should not obscure the fact that the United Kingdom still produces some excellent missile systems which continue to provide the British Armed Forces with excellent weapons. Sea Eagle, Rapier and the already-mentioned Sky Flash are in the forefront of their kind and seem set fair to continue to do so for many years ahead.

ALARM

Body diameter Not released. **Fin span** Not released. **Length** Not released. **Weight at launch** 180 kg. **Weight of warhead** Not released. **Maximum range** 10 km plus. **Minimum range** Estimated 1 km. **Velocity** Mach 1 plus. **Carrier vehicles** See text.

The ALARM (Air-Launched Anti-Radar Missile) was developed under the auspices of a British requirement for a missile to suppress enemy radar during deep penetration missions. It is initally destined for the Royal Air Force Tornado GR 1 and Buccaneer S 2 fleets, but is being adapted for the Royal Navy's planned Sea Harrier FRS 2 and even for use in modern battlefield helicopters, such as the British Army's planned LAH programme. Service entry is reported to be 1987.

The missile is guided in flight by a broadband passive radar seeker, developed by Marconi and powered by a two-stage, solid-fuelled motor. The missile homes on the selected radar emissions of a target, particularly those of anti-aircraft missile defences. The missile is manoeuvred in flight by means of the cruciform wings located

The primary role of ALARM is to suppress the radar systems of enemy surface-to-air missile sites during a deep penetration interdiction. The Tornado GR 1 shown is carrying seven ALARM on fuselage and wing mountings, together with the BOZ-107 counter-measures dispenser (starboard wing) and the Marconi Sky Shadow ECM pod (port wing) (BAe).

ALARM can also be carried by helicopters, such as the Westland Navy Lynx. Although the Fleet Air Arm has not been supplied with the anti-radiation missile, trials have apparently been carried out with dummy rounds (Robin Adshead).

amidships, with fixed stabilizing fins aft.

A normal sortie might include several aircraft armed with ALARM as well as other ordnance. The missile is pre-briefed before departure with a list of priority targets, using the memory software, and the missile's seeker will begin searching for such radar emissions immediately after launch from the carrying aircraft. The pilot/navigation systems operator will have already identified a threat using his onboard electronic surveillance equipment.

For certain missions, the ALARM can be programmed for a high altitude drop and will then loiter on a parachute whilst the seeker finds the highest value emitter — this is known as the search, evaluation and acquisition sequence. When the target has been acquired, the parachute is released and the motor takes the missile to the target.

AMRAAM

Body diameter 0.18 m. **Fin span (tail)** 0.63 m. **Length** 3.65 m. **Weight at launch** Approx 150 kg. **Weight of warhead** Estimated 22 kg. **Maximum range** 25 km plus. **Minimum range** Approx 3 km. **Velocity** Mach 1 plus. **Carrier vehicles** See text.

The Advanced Medium-Range Air-to-Air Missile (AMRAAM) is being developed by Hughes Aircraft Corporation under the designation AIM-120A and will be the replacement for the Sparrow system. The development of the missile will be by the United States, whilst the advanced short-range version, ASRAAM (qv), is being worked on in Europe. It i anticipated that AMRAAM will be operational on the Sea Harrier FRS 2, Tornado F 3 and other air defence aircraft after 1989. The Sea Harrier will carry up to four of the missiles on wing pylons.

The development programme calls for the missile to operate in all weathers, all aspects, and to be radar-guided to intercept large formations of enemy aircraft approaching a defended area, but out of visual range. The system is all-but a fire-and-forget missile of medium range.

Before launching the missile will be given all available data and after leaving the fighter's launching rail, the AMRAAM will feed back information to the pilot, before the terminal phase of the flight when the radar seeker is activated and intercepts the target.

AS 12

Body diameter 0.18 m. **Fin span** 0.65 m. **Length** 1.87 m. **Weight at launch** 76 kg. **Weight of warhead** 10 kg. **Maximum range** 8 km. **Minimum range** 500 m. **Maximum velocity** 300 m/s. **Carrier vehicles** See text.

The Nord AS 12 is a wire-guided missile which, although it achieved fame during the liberation of South Georgia in 1982, (Operation 'Paraquat'), is no longer fully operational with the British forces. In the Royal Navy, the AS 12 has been carried by the Westland Wasp HAS 1 helicopter for anti-shipping strikes and by the Westland Wessex HU 5 for anti-tank operations. In the British Army, the earlier SS 11 missile was operational until 1985.

The AS 12 is a lightweight, wire-guided missile for multi-purpose strikes and was used by the Royal Navy in its operations against the Argentine naval submarine, *Santa Fe*, found on the surface off South Georgia at the beginning of the Falklands' conflict. The missile thus became the first to be launched in anger by the Royal Navy and at least five hits were made against the submarine.

When carried aboard the Wasp, a specially designed carrier is fitted to the helicopter on which up to four missile in total can be loaded. This role change operation takes about five to fifteen minutes, depending on the previous weapons' fit, and it is normal for the Wasp to be armed with the missiles prior to entering the engagement zone. In that case, the helicopter would be armed and fuelled, ready to launch. The AS 12 requires the use of a special sight, mounted on the port side of the cabin roof. The sight, a SFIM M260, is operated by the helicopter's aircrewman and he uses it to aim the missile, whilst electrical impulses are passed to the missile's cruciform control fins via the command wire. Flight time can be up to twenty seconds.

All embarked flights of Wasp in 'Leander', 'Rothesay' and 'Hecla' Class vessels have the ability to carry AS 12 but some ships may not have the missile load, depending on role. The missile and the helicopter will phase out of British service by 1989.

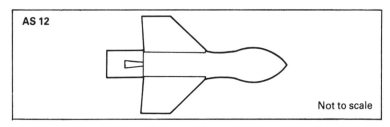

AS 12

Not to scale

ASRAAM

Body diameter Not released. **Fin span** Not released. **Length** Not released. **Weight** Approx 120 kg. **Weight of warhead** Approx 5 kg. **Maximum range** Approx 5 km. **Minimum range** Approx 1 km. **Maximum velocity** Mach 3 plus. **Carrier vehicles** See text.

The Advanced Short-Range Air-to-Air Missile (ASRAAM) programme is currently underway to provide the European NATO nations and the United States with a replacement missile for the AIM-9 Sidewinder family in the early- to mid-1990s. The project is being run by an Anglo-German consortium of British Aerospace and Bodenseewerk Geratetechnik, with advice being offered by Hughes Aircraft Company (USA) and Aerospatiale (France) as an observer.

ASRAAM will be a fire-and-forget missile of great agility capable of being launched at long stand-off range and to attack targets from all aspects. Feasibility studies were completed in 1983. The missile will arm the Royal Navy's Sea Harrier FRS 2 force, as well as the RAF's Tornado F 3s and Phantoms.

In addition, British Aerospace is working alone on a series of high velocity (Mach 3) and hyper velocity (Mach 5 to 6) 'hittiles' for the next decade. These missiles, known by the family name of Thunderbolt, have been planned with Falklands' conflict experience and will be small and light enough for battlefield helicopters and for ground troop use. In the distant future, there is the SRARM missile project for a combination role missile.

To replace the Sidewinder for close-range missile engagements, it is presumed that the Fleet Air Arm will be equipped with the AIM-132 ASRAAM (Advanced Short-Range Air-to-Air Missile). In addition, the UK Air Defence force of Phantom and Tornado aircraft will be equipped with the missile, built by a European consortium, in the late 1990s. It is shown during tests on a Sea Harrier FRS 1 of 899 Squadron, but will enter service on the FRS 2 variant (BAe).

BLOODHOUND MARK 2

Maximum body diameter 0.546 m. **Fin span** 2.83 m. **Length** 8.46 m. **Weight** Not available. **Range** Approx 80 km. **Velocity** Mach 2.

The Bloodhound Mark 2 is now one of the oldest air defence guided missile systems still in service with the NATO forces for it can trace its origins back to the early 1950s. It was originally provided with the code name of 'Red Duster' and the Royal Air Force received its first examples in 1958. That was the Mark 1 but in the same year the development of the improved Mark 2 commenced and these began to be installed in 1964. They have now replaced all the earlier Marks in service. The overall

An RAF Police dog handler and his charge patrol the Bloodhound Mark 2 installations at RAF West Raynham (MoD).

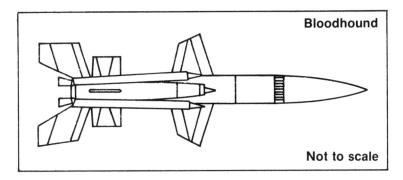

Bloodhound

Not to scale

system contractor today is the British Aerospace Dynamics Group at Bristol.

The Bloodhound Mark 2s are all based along the eastern side of the United Kingdom for the defence of the air bases in that region. In earlier years they were deployed in locations overseas, Cyprus being one important Bloodhound base and West Germany another. In the UK today they are located on a number of what are virtually static emplacements since, although the Bloodhound Mark 2 system can be moved if required, it can take quite a time.

In action the Bloodhounds are alerted by a long-range surveillance radar when aircraft targets approach. This information is passed to a section of four or eight missiles with its own target illuminating radar (TIR) and launch control post (LCP). The TIR, a radar known as Firelight, is directed towards the target by the surveillance radar and the reflected energy produced by the TIR can then be used to direct the missile to its target. The missile is launched at the appropriate moment by the LCP, using data from a high capacity computer. This computer also acts as the fire control computer and monitors the various missiles' state of readiness for firing and other 'in house' tasks.

On firing, the Bloodhound Mark 2 is launched by the force provided by four solid-propellant rocket booster motors. Once sufficient velocity has been reached two Rolls-Royce Bristol Thor ramjets cut in to power the missile. Flight guidance for the Bloodhound Mark 2 is of the twist-and-steer variety using stub wing fins, guidance towards the target being provided by the reflected radar energy from the TIR. Once close to the target the high explosive warhead is detonated by a proximity fuze. The maximum range of the Bloodhound Mark 2 is about 80 km and targets flying as low as 300 m have been engaged in tests.

There is as yet no sign of the Bloodhound Mark 2s being removed or phased out of service. As late as 1978 plans were announced to keep

Bloodhound Mark 2 on its launching post and ready to fire (RAFG PR).

the missiles in service for some years to come, so there is obviously a good deal of life left in them yet. At the moment the Bloodhound Mark 2s are deployed under the control of two squadrons (Nos 25 and 85) of No 11 Group with their administrative and engineering base at RAF West Raynham.

BLOWPIPE AND JAVELIN

Blowpipe body diameter 0.076 m. **Fin span** 0.274 m. **Length** 1.349 m. **Weight of system** 20.67 kg. **Maximum range** 3,000 m plus. **Maximum velocity** Not released but supersonic.

Blowpipe was originally a private venture project developed by Short Brothers plc of Belfast using know-how derived from their Seacat and Tigercat missile systems. It was selected as the British Army's one-man anti-aircraft missile system in 1966 and ever since has been in service with the Royal Artillery's low level air defence batteries, both Regular and TA, and was used with considerable success during the 1982 Falkland Islands' campaign (by both sides).

Blowpipe is a shoulder-launched weapon that is fired and guided by one man. The missile is contained in a sealed canister which can be handled exactly like any piece of conventional ammunition until the time comes to use it. The container tube than has the aiming unit clipped on to its body and the missile is ready to fire — this takes only a few seconds. The firer points the missile towards the target using the aiming unit and when ready presses a trigger. A primary rocket motor then launches the missile from the container tube after which a secondary motor cuts in to

Cut-away view of Blowpipe on a demonstration model showing how the missile's rear fins are housed in the front part of the launcher. When it is fired, they slide to the rear and unfold.

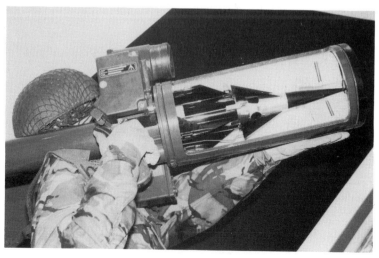

Blowpipe deployed in the field.

propel it towards the target. Using the aiming unit monocular sight and a flare in the missile's tail, the firer then guides the missile towards the target via a radio link, utilizing a thumb-operated joystick to operate the missile's small canard wings. When near or on the target a proximity or contact fuze detonates the warhead. If it misses, the missile self-destructs. The aiming unit can then be removed from the spent container tube and used on another missile container.

Blowpipe has proved to be a very accurate system and has been widely exported to a number of countries. It is still in production but has now been largely replaced in British Army service by a newer system

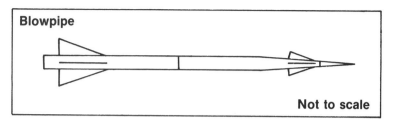

Blowpipe

Not to scale

known as Javelin. Javelin is based on Blowpipe and uses a virtually identical missile with an improved rocket motor. The main change is to the guidance system which no longer uses the small awkward thumb joystick but a method known technically as SACLOS (semi-automatic command line-of-sight). This involves a new aiming unit, and all the firer has to do is keep the target in the centre of the sight — the SACLOS system transmits all guidance command signals to the missile automatically. Javelin is otherwise handled and fired in the same manner as Blowpipe but other improvements include a more powerful motor and an improved fuze to give the missile a maximum range of over 4,000 m. Early experience gained with Javelin has shown that it is even more accurate than Blowpipe with some training ranges running out of target drones long before previous expectations.

Within the low-level air defence batteries in BAOR the Blowpipe/Javelin teams are carried around in FV103 Spartan armoured personnel carriers fitted with internal racks for the missile containers. UK-based

Javelin, showing the new SACLOS guidance system, and also demonstrating how the missile's fins slide to the rear after firing.

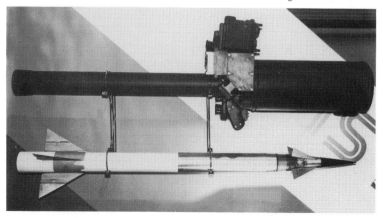

Now developed for such vessels as Royal Fleet Auxiliaries, a variant of the Shorts Lightweight Multiple Launcher (LML) for the Javelin system (Shorts).

batteries use specially equipped Land-Rovers. Short Bros have developed multiple launchers for both Blowpipe and Javelin which can be mounted on vehicles or used on tripods or other ground mountings, but the future of these within the British Army is uncertain.

However, even the advanced Javelin is now regarded only as an interim missile pending the introduction of a new system that is currently under development. This is known provisionally as the High Velocity Missile System (HVMS) which uses a missile with a velocity so high (well over Mach 4) that it is virtually an aim-and-shoot system almost like a gun. At the time of writing a development contract had yet to be awarded but several companies are known to be in the running, including Short Bros and British Aerospace Dynamics Systems. The former is proposing Starstreak and latter is proposing a system known as Thunderbolt.

EXOCET

Body diameter 0.348 m. **Fin span** 1.0 m. **Length** 5.2 m. **Weight at launch** 735 kg. **Weight of warhead** Approx 165 kg. **Maximum range** 42 km. **Minimum range** 2 km. **Maximum velocity** Approx Mach 0.85. **Carrier vehicles** See text.

Few people had heard of the Aerospatiale Exocet anti-shipping missile until May 1982, when the air-launched version, AM39, was used with great effect against the Royal Navy's task group around the Falkland Islands; the missile caused the loss of *Sheffield* and *Atlantic Conveyor*. What many failed to realize then (certainly in the Fleet Street media), was that the Royal Navy was one of the major export customers for the ship-launched version, MM38, and that consideration was being given to the uprated supersonic MM40 version for the Type 23 frigate programme. In the event, and perhaps not unconnected with the Falklands (where several Exocets were successfully decoyed by the RN), the Harpoon system was chosen instead.

In the early 1970s, the UK Ministry of Defence turned to France for the purchase of an 'off-the-shelf' surface-to-surface missile to enhance the over-the-horizon capability of the Royal Navy's surface combat units. Frigates of the 'Amazon' and 'Leander' Classes were needed to supplement the existing Surface Action Groups (SAGs) as part of the NATO defence of the Eastern Atlantic. The missile was attractive to the British government because small sub-assemblies were manufactured in the UK and because of its good high subsonic, very low-level performance.

The presumed threats to the SAGs and the larger surface escorts, like the 'County' Class guided missile destroyers (four of which were refitted with Exocet), were the smaller corvettes and fast patrol boats armed with stand-off surface-to-surface weapons with ranges in excess of 20 km. The speed of reaction of the canister-mounted Exocet missiles would have been important in the decision-making process. The choice was made in 1976 but was very much a stop-gap for the Type 21 frigates, which had been criticized for their lack of surface action armament.

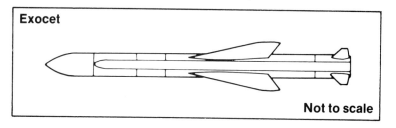

Exocet

Not to scale

Background photograph *The Exocet missile provides certain of the Royal Navy's surface combat ships with an over-the-horizon capability against a number of threat types. The Batch 2 'County' Class guided missile destroyers were refitted with Exocet in place of 'B' turret, and here a missile is seen immediately after launch (RN).*

Inset *The major drawback with Exocet is that it is fitted to warships in non-reloadable canister mountings and so the ship is limited to four missiles only. Very often, one would imagine that all four would be ripple-launched against a threat during a surface action. This is* Norfolk, *a destroyer sold to Chile in 1981 (RN).*

The Batch 2 'Leader' Class frigates have the Exocet system in place of their 114 mm (4.5-in) gun turret, as shown by Sirius, *seen entering Portsmouth* (Paul Beaver).

The first 'Leander' to be converted was *Cleopatra* in 1972-75, and subsequently all the Batch 2 warships of the class were converted to mount Exocet instead of the Mk 6 114 mm (4.5 in) gun turret for'ard of the bridge: *Minerva* (1976-79); *Danae (1977-78); Argonaut* (1978-80); and *Penelope* (1978-80). *Juno* was refitted without Exocet for Fleet Training duties from 1981-85.

The last of the Type 21 or 'Amazon' Class frigates to receive Exocet was *Ambuscade*, during her 1984-85 refit, whilst the four 'County' Class Batch 2 destroyers were modified to take Exocet instead of the 114 mm Mk 6 'B' turret, with only *Fife* and *Glamorgan* remaining in service; *Norfolk* and *Antrim* were sold to Chile in 1981 and 1984 respectively. The Exocet launchers are single weapon systems, with no re-loads carried aboard the warship.

To launch Exocet against a potential target, the warship's own fire control system, is connected to the ITS (*Installation de Tir Standard*) which provides data to the inertial navigation system carried aboard each missile. To aid the homing of the missile in the last 10 km or so, the Exocet is fitted with an active homing radar. The warship is unable to train the fixed mountings, so must turn into the Exocet firing window. It would be normal practice to fire at least two missiles at a target before withdrawal out of range; Exocet is a fire-and-forget missile with total autonomy and very high hit probability.

HARPOON

Body diameter 0.343 m. **Fin span** 0.76 m. **Length** 4.635 m. **Weight at launch** 681.9 kg. **Weight of warhead** 221.6 kg. **Maximum range** 90 km plus. **Minimum range** Approx 1 km. **Velocity** High subsonic **Carrier vehicles** See text.

This ship-launched missile system has been ordered by the Royal Navy from the makers, McDonnell Douglas, for the Type 23 frigates. The missile will become the standard anti-ship missile and may also arm the Type 22 Batch 3 frigates also under construction. The missile itself is identical to the Sub-Harpoon system already in service with the Submarine Flotilla of the Royal Navy. The Royal Naval version differs from that used by the US and other friendly navies in that it has an advanced guidance system which allows it to surface skim at lower altitudes than possible before. It is thought the RN version, due to enter service in about 1988, will have quadruple launchers and the missile can be launched within an envelope of +90° of the target's bearing.

The American-built and manufactured RGM-84 Harpoon missile has been chosen for the last Type 22 and Type 23 frigates of the Royal Navy. A USN warship demonstrates the missile during an exercise in 1983; the version illustrated is known as an anti-ship cruise missile by the USN (McDonnell Douglas)

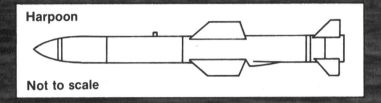

Harpoon

Not to scale

An interesting picture, showing the McDonnell Douglas Harpoon missile immediately after launch from it special canister. The anti-shipping weapon is in widespread use around the world and will enter RN service shortly (McDonnell Douglas).

IKARA

Body diameter Not released. **Fin span** 1.52 m. **Length** 3.42 m. **Height** 1.57 m. **Weight overall** Classified. **Maximum range** Approx 24 km. **Minimum range** Approx 3 km. **Maximum velocity** Approx Mach 0.8. **Carrier vehicles** See text.

Although generally considered to be a missile, and described as such for the purposes of this book, the Anglo-Australian Ikara is really a delivery vehicle for anti-submarine warfare (ASW) torpedoes. It is described by British Aerospace, who act as general sales agents, as a long-range, anti-submarine weapon system, originally designed and developed by several Australian Governmental departments.

The Ikara is powered by a solid-fuelled motor to take it to a pre-determined drop position, where the ASW torpedo is released to home on the target submarine beneath the surface. The launch position in British warships is called the gazebo, a housing for'ard of the bridge of certain 'Leander' Class frigates and the destroyer *Bristol*. The launcher, although it can train through about 180°, is fixed in a launch angle of 55°.

Target information for Ikara is obtained through the ship's long-range passive or active sonar equipment, or through the services of aerial units, such as ASW helicopters. The data is analyzed in the operations room and fed into the Ikara computer. In turn this computer gives the best possible drop position for the Ikara, and a drop can be made regardless of weather conditions. The position has been identified relative to ship's course and speed, as well as wind and timings.

Photographed in 1975, the Ikara guided weapon system, armed here with the Mk 44 anti-submarine warfare torpedo which equips Batch 1 'Leander' Class frigates and Bristol. *Although the system has proved to be successful, it will not be updated* (Paul Beaver).

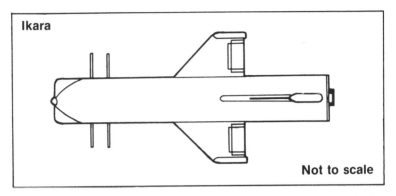

Ikara

Not to scale

The ship's radar will track and pass course corrections to the missile, whilst launch vectors will have already been passed to the missile's own guidance system.

Using automatic handling, plus the attentions of two ratings to fit the cruciform winglets, the Ikara is made ready for launch. Using the trainable launcher, the missile is moved into the correct sector. The Ikara is always stored with the ASW torpedo attached. Torpedoes which can be carried by the Ikara include the Royal Navy's Mk 44, Mk 46 and Stingray (the latter just entering service); the TP42 (Sweden); A244/S (Italy); and Type 73 (Japan). The Ikara 2 programme to uprate the existing British systems has been abandoned in favour of other systems, including modern helicopters, such as Lynx and Sea King Mk 5/6, fitted with the Stingray ASW torpedo.

During trials aboard the first Ikara-Leander, Leander *fired a number of the Anglo-Australian Ikara systems to prove its capability for carrying ASW torpedoes to long ranges for anti-submarine warfare* (RN).

LANCE

Body diameter 0.557 mm. **Fin span** Not released. **Length** 6.146 m. **Weight at launch** 1,285.47 kg. **Weight of warhead (M234)** 210.92 kg. **Maximum range** 121 km. **Minimum range** 4.8 km. **Maximum velocity** Mach 3 plus. **Maximum flight time** 200 seconds. **Maximum altitude** 45,720 m. **Carrier vehicle** M752 Self-Propelled Launcher (SPL) — 1 missile.

In artillery terms, Lance is the British Army's most powerful weapon for it is a ballistic missile carrying a nuclear warhead. It is an American design originally produced by a large number of defence contractors under the leadership of the LTV Aerospace Corporation, now known as the Vought Corporation.

Lance has undergone some designation changes. When the first firing was made in 1965 it was simply known as the Missile B but it was later re-named the MGM-52C. The British Army got its first examples in 1976 and Lance has been deployed in BAOR ever since, organized into a single four-battery Missile Regiment under the direct control of the Commander 1 (BR) Corps.

Lance is a free-flight missile that does not have any form of external guidance once it has been launched. When it is in the air there is no way that an enemy can jam guidance signals or interfere with the flight path. This does not mean that Lance is unguided, for it is, but all guidance data is fed into the missile just prior to the launch. Once in its carefully-selected firing position the rocket body is aligned with its target using normal artillery techniques. Flight information is then fed into the missile inertial guidance system from a solid state programmer known as the AN/GJM-24 (XO-2) which then monitors and controls the launch and provides the pre-flight electrical power supplies. On firing, a liquid-propellant rocket boost motor gives the main launch power for a period of 1.5 to 6 seconds, depending on the range required, after which a smaller rocket motor takes over. Flight stabilization is provided by spin generated by inclined jets tapped off from the main booster motor. The inertial guidance system uses its data and pre-programmed directions to determine when the motor should be cut off and the missile then continues its journey in free flight. British Army Lance missiles use nuclear warheads only, but some other NATO armies have conventional high explosive or bomblet-carrying warheads.

Lance missiles are carried to their firing point on a tracked carrier known as the M752 Self-Propelled Launcher, or SPL. This carrier also acts as the launch vehicle and carries the launch crew of six men. A similar vehicle, known as the M688 Loader-Transporter or LT, carries a further two Lance missiles with their tail fins removed and stowed

Above *Preparing a Lance for launch from its M752 Self-Propelled Launcher (SPL).*
Right *Rear view of a Lance elevated prior to launch.*

alongside their bodies. The LT has a crew of two and uses a small crane to load the missiles on to the SPL for launching. Data for the SPL and LT, which are basically the same vehicle based on the American M113 armoured personnel carrier, is as follows:

Weight in action, SPL 9,075 kg. **Weight in action, LT** 10,691.63 kg. **Length** 6.568 m. **Width** 2.709 m. **Height, top of cab** 2.715 m. **Engine** GMC Model 6V-53 V-6 diesel developing 210 bhp at 2,800 rpm **Maximum road speed** 64 km/h. **Range** 450 km.

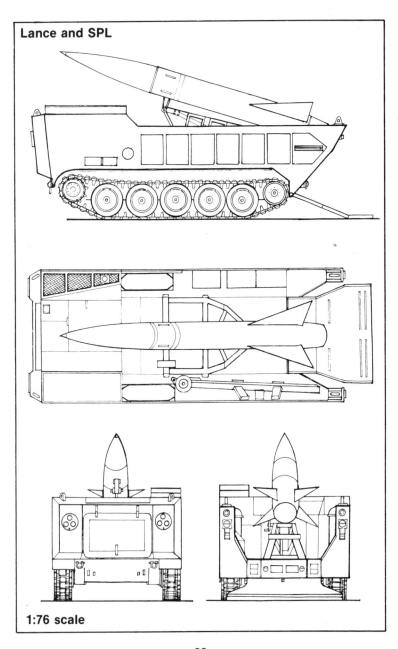

Lance and SPL

1:76 scale

Above *A Hughes AIM-120A Advanced Medium-Range Air-to-Air Missile together with an ASRAAM and a Sea Eagle in front of a Sea Harrier.*

Below *A Royal Navy Wasp helicopter fitted with AS 12 wire-guided missiles similar to those which crippled the Argentine submarine* Santa Fe *in 1982.*

Above *Exocet launchers on the bow of HMS* Phoebe, *a 'Leander' Class frigate.*
Right *A Polaris missile being loaded aboard a 'Resolution' Class nuclear submarine.*
Below *A Lance missile being readied for firing from its M752 self-propelled launch vehicle.*

Left *A Rapier installation prior to a firing trial by men of the RAF Regiment at the Benbecula in the Hebrides.*

Below *A Shorts Seacat being launched from a 'Leander' Class frigate.*

LAW 80

Body diameter (calibre) 0.094 m. **Fin span** Not released. **Launcher length, open** Approx 1.5 m. **Launcher length, closed** Approx 1 m. **Weight carried** 9.6 kg. **Weight at firing** 8.8 kg. **Weight of projectile** Approx 4 kg. **Maximum range** 500 m. **Minimum range** 20 m. **Armour penetration** Over 600 mm.

LAW 80 is the usual term used for the Light Anti-armour Weapon 80, the British Army's latest anti-tank weapon. LAW 80 is scheduled to be issued at all levels throughout the British Army from front-line units to support services and will provide every soldier with the means to defeat enemy armour.

LAW 80 has been designed to replace the Rocket 66 mm HEAT L1A1 with the British Armed Forces. Like the L1A1, LAW 80 had to be easy to use and carry but it also required a warhead large enough to ensure that it would pierce the thick armoured carapaces of modern tanks. The choice of a 94 mm warhead has thus been interesting, for at first sight this calibre is not large enough — even TOW with its 155 mm calibre is now considered too small for the task. On LAW 80 this deficiency has been overcome by careful and thorough design of the warhead and, although the exact form of this design has not been disclosed

LAW 80 ready for firing.

(understandably), it is stated to be more than capable of penetrating over 600 mm of armour plate.

The LAW 80 warhead is carried to its target by a rocket fired from a tube. Like the earlier L1A1, the LAW 80 launcher telescopes down in size but it is not as handy as the earlier weapon due mainly to the bulk involved. The filament-wound tube launcher is itself a fairly complex piece of engineering that is supplied with a carrying handling and prominent carriage seals at each end. These have to be removed before used and before telescoping the weapon into the open position. Opening the weapon moves the centre of gravity from the handle to an over-the-shoulder firing position (an example of the extreme care taken in the design of this weapon) and also allows the simple optical sight to flip into position.

To ensure that aiming the LAW 80 will be as effective as possible at the longer ranges involved, the launcher has a spotting rifle incorporated. Before the rocket is launched, aiming is checked by firing spotter rounds from this rifle and observing their fall on the target. If they strike the target they provide a momentary flash indication, denoting that the aim is correct. The spotter rifle contains five rounds all ready for use with no loading involved by the firer, and it is considered that these will be sufficient for two engagements. If, for any reason, it is not decided to fire the rocket during one engagement the LAW 80 can be folded up again for re-use. If the rocket is fired the launcher can be discarded.

LAW 80 is issued as a standard piece of ammunition and requires no preparation for use other than removing the end seals and opening. It will be used by the Army, the Royal Marines and the Royal Air Force Regiment. At the time of writing the main question is 'when?'. Hunting Engineering have had LAW 80 in their design hands for many years and their care can be seen in every aspect of its handling and performance but as yet it is not in production, although reports of its imminence have been current for some time. The British Army badly needs a viable portable anti-tank weapon that will provide all levels of the Army with the means to penetrate up to 600 mm of enemy tank armour at ranges up to 500 m so let us hope it is not too long before LAW 80 is in large-scale service with the British Armed Forces.

MARTEL

Body diameter 0.4 m. **Fin span** Approx 1.2 m. **Length (AS 37)** 4.12 m; **(AJ 168)** 3.87 m. **Weight (AS 37)** 550 kg; **(AJ 168)** 530 kg. **Weight of warhead** 150 kg (?). **Maximum range** Estimated 60 km. **Velocity** Mach 0.9 plus. **Carrier vehicle** Buccaneer S Mark 2B — up to 4 missiles.

Considering the length of time that Martel has been in service, remarkably little 'hard' data has been disclosed, possibly due to its international origins for Martel is an Anglo-French anti-shipping missile produced in two versions, one radar-seeking (AS 37) and the other having a video guidance system (AJ 168).

The radar-guided Martel is a French responsibility with the main contractor being Engins Matra. The video-guided version is the AJ 168 that was developed in the United Kingdom by the British Aerospace Dynamics Group with Marconi Avionic Systems providing the video guidance system. The AJ 168 and the AS 37 are both used by the Royal Air Force shipping strike squadrons equipped with Buccaneer S 2Bs — the French do not employ the video-guided AJ 168.

The AS 37 radar-guided version of Martel fitted to an RAF Buccaneer S 2 strike aircraft (MoD).

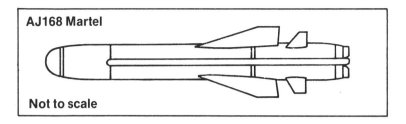

AJ168 Martel

Not to scale

Martel is an extremely powerful anti-shipping weapon with a warhead that has been estimated as weighing 150 kg. It has an estimated range of 60 km when launched from high altitude, about half this when launched at 'wave top' height. After launch an integral autopilot provides guidance along one of several possible pre-programmed flight profiles until the video or radar guidance system can be brought into play. The radar-guidance system has the advantage of being passive and not subject to interference unless the enemy realise that they are under attack and simply switch off all their radars — which will often render them 'blind' and unoperational. The video guidance system is not prone to this hazard for one of the launch aircraft crew members can provide some of the final guidance using visual and other data obtained from a small video camera located in the missile's nose. These information and guidance signals are transmitted along a data link between the missile and the launch aircraft.

Martel has been around since 1964 and it is now regarded as getting a bit long in the tooth. It is still a very powerful anti-shipping weapon but technology has made considerable strides since 1964 and eventually Martel will be supplemented and eventually replaced by Sea Eagle.

Left *The AJ168 version of Martel showing the video camera panel in the nose* (MoD).

41

MIDGE

Body diameter 0.33 m. **Fin span** 0.94 m. **Length with booster** 3.73 m. **Length in flight** 2.6 m. **Range** Up to 160 km. **Maximum Velocity** 740 km/h (400 kt). **Operational altitude** 300 to 1,200 m. **Carrier vehicle** Bedford Mk 4,000 kg (4 × 4) truck — 1 drone.

The Midge is not a guided missile in the generally accepted sense for it is a pilotless aircraft that comes into the general category of remotely piloted vehicle (RPV) or drone. It is used by the British Army as an airborne battlefield surveillance platform to enable artillery batteries to locate potential targets well behind enemy lines. It can also be used for general intelligence-gathering purposes.

The Midge was originally a Canadian design known as the Canadair CL-89. Later the United Kingdom became involved and eventually West Germany as well, so it became something of an international programme. The present approved designation is AN/USD-501 but the British Army calls it the Midge.

The Midge is normally carried by a Bedford MK 4-tonne truck which also acts as its launcher vehicle. Before a flight the Midge's chosen flight path is pre-programmed into the flight control system, usually in the form of a circular or elliptical pattern. The Midge is then launched using a rocket booster motor which burns for two seconds before a small turbojet takes over. During its flight path the Midge uses its sensor pack at pre-selected intervals. This sensor pack might use either a Carl Zeiss KRG 8/24 stereoscopic tri-lens camera or a British Aerospace Dynamics infra-red Linescan Type 201, either of which can cover large

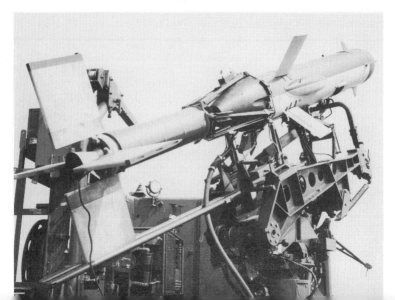

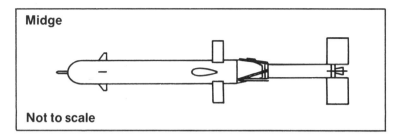

Midge

Not to scale

areas of terrain below. At night, flares can be ejected to illuminate the surrounding area for the camera.

As the Midge returns to its launch site it is homed-in by radio beacons up to the point where the engine shuts down and parachutes are deployed to lower it to the ground. Air bags are inflated in the nose to reduce the shock of landing. Once recovered, the sensor pack is hurriedly removed for processing to discover its information. The Midge can be re-used.

Unfortunately for the user arm, the Royal Artillery, the Midge is now obsolescent. It is too slow and it takes too long for its information to be processed. More modern RPVs transmit their information when they are still in flight over their target areas and are much faster in order to elude enemy defences. During recent years there have been many attempts to provide the Royal Artillery with a more up-to-date surveillance drone system but most have come to naught, usually on cost grounds. However, a replacement for the Midge is now in prospect and known as Phoenix, but until this arrives the Midge will remain in service.

Left *A Midge unfolded on its launcher. The rocket booster motor in the foreground falls away two seconds after launch.*

Right *A drill Midge round on a Royal Artillery Land Rover showing the appearance of the missile without its booster rocket.*

MILAN

Warhead diameter 0.115 m. **Body diameter (min)** 0.090 m. **Fin diameter** 0.265 m. **Length of missile** 0.769 m. **Length of missile container** 1.26 m. **Weight of missile** 6.65 kg. **Weight of warhead** 2.98 kg with fuze. **Weight of warhead charge** 1.45 kg. **Weight of missile and container** 11.5 kg. **Weight of launch unit** 15.5 kg. **Maximum range** 2,000 m. **Minimum range** 25 m. **Velocity** 75 to 200 m/s. **Time of flight to 2,000 m** Up to 13 seconds. **Armour penetration** Up to 352 mm. **Carrier vehicle** FV103 Spartan with MCT — 2 missiles.

The origins of the Milan anti-tank missile are French, and its Milan is derived from 'Missile d'Infantrie Leger Anti-Char'. It has been in production since 1972 with a French-West German consortium known as Euromissile and the first British Army contracts were placed in 1975. Ever since then Milan has been one of the British Army's most important anti-tank weapons for it is the principal long-range anti-armour weapon of the foot soldier.

In its basic infantry form the Milan missile is fired from a small but rather bulky launcher — the Army refers to these as 'firing posts'. The missiles themselves are issued in sealed containers that require no maintenance or preparation and clip on to the launchers when required. In the field the launcher is mounted on a low tripod and the firer uses a periscopic sight to observe the target and aim the missile. British Army Milan launchers now also have a thermal imaging sight known as MIRA for use at night or in poor visibility.

When the firer acquired a target he can fire the missile which is pushed out of its container by a gas generator in the base of the container tube. The same gas pressure also propels the empty tube off the launcher and to the rear to allow another container to be clipped on if required. After the missile has 'coasted' far enough from the launcher to avoid the rocket exhaust harming the firer (and to prevent the exhaust signature from indicating the precise position of the launcher) the rocket

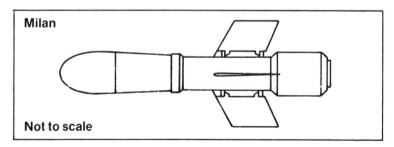

Milan

Not to scale

The new Milan Compact Turret (MCT) fitted to an Army Spartan armoured personnel carrier.

motor ignites to provide the main propulsion. At the same time four fins spring out from the body to provide flight stability and the guidance wire unwinds from a bobbin in the missile tail (the wire is less than 0.4 mm thick). Small flares around the tail enable the firer to track the Milan missile to its quarry but the actual guidance is automatic once the firer has pin-pointed the tank target using an illuminated graticule in the sight. The Milan's shaped charge warhead can disable most current armour, but with the move to heavier armour on many of the latest tanks there are plan to somehow improve the Milan's anti-armour performance. During the Falkland Islands' campaign Milan missiles were sometimes used as 'bunker busters'.

Milan is a one-man weapon but the British Army uses two-man teams (one man carries the spare missile containers) with two teams to a section. In BAOR these sections are carried into battle in FV432s but they dismount for action. One innovation that will soon appear in BAOR is that a number of extra FV103 Spartans will be issued to each battalion. These will have a small roof-mounted turret equipped with two Milan launchers that can be fired and guided from within the vehicle; these are known as Milan Compact Turrets, or MCTs. The number of Milan firing posts to a battalion will depend on the type of battalion involved. Most United Kingdom-based battalions have as few as six while 6 Airmobile Brigade in BAOR has as many as 48.

Most Milans used by the British Armed Forces (the Royal Marines are also equipped with the weapon) have been manufactured by the British Aerospace Dynamics Group at Stevenage.

MULTIPLE LAUNCH ROCKET SYSTEM (MLRS)

Body diameter 0.227 m. **Length** 3.96 m. **Weight at launch** 308 kg. **Maximum range** 30,000 m plus.

Carrier vehicle — Armament 12 × 227 mm ballistic rockets. **Crew** 3. **Weight in action** 25,191 kg. **Length travelling** 6.972 m. **Height travelling** 2.617 m. **Height, launcher elevated** 5.92 m. **Width travelling** 2.972 m. **Track width** 0.533 m. **Ground clearance** 0.43 m. **Maximum road speed** 64 km/h. **Range, roads** 483 km. **Vertical obstacle** 0.914 m. **Maximum gradient** 60 %. **Trench crossing** 2.29 m. **Fording** 1.02 m. **Engine** Cummins VTA-903 turbocharged 8-cylinder diesel developing 500 bhp at 2,400 rpm. **Ammunition stowage** 12 × 227 mm rockets on launcher.

The Multiple Launch Rocket System, or MLRS as it is usually known, started life as an American project but has now blossomed into an international programme. It was originally a 1976 US Army project that involved a 'shoot-off' between various designs and concepts until the system emerged in its present form in 1980. Since then MLRS has entered service with the US Army but its planned introduction into service by other NATO nations, including the United Kingdom, West Germany, Italy and France, has been beset by the glitches that

Cut-away drawing of an MLRS rocket.

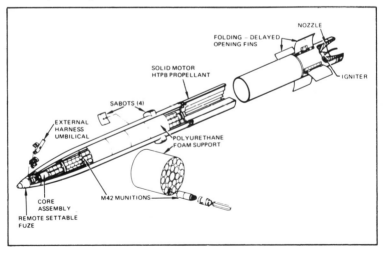

An MLRS rocket being fired from an American Army launch vehicle similar to those which will be used by the British Army.

international defence projects seem to engender. The NATO project has been delayed further by the fact that it is planned to produce MLRS in Europe and by the 'who does what' division of the production contracts.

To date the British Army has received only four training MLRS systems and at the time of writing even they were still 'in the supply system'. The current plan is that the Army will start to get its MLRS equipments during 1988 but even this forecast may turn out to be somewhat optimistic as the European production plans are still in their early stages. However, the Army is anxious to obtain MLRS as soon as possible for it will be one of the most important NATO land weapon systems of the coming decade.

MLRS has been developed to provide a powerful long-range artillery system that will literally cover the rear areas behind enemy lines with fire. To do this MLRS fires a 227 mm ballistic rocket to a range over 30,000 m

MLRS launch vehicle

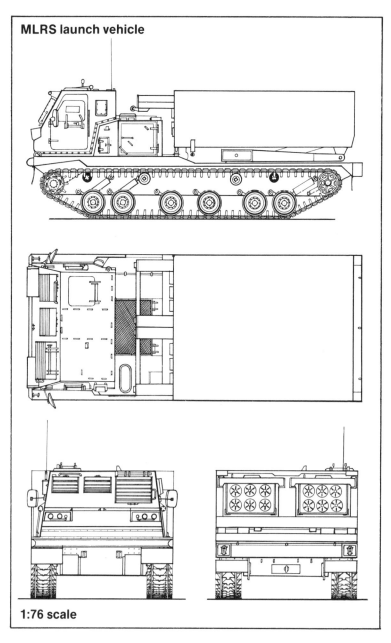

1:76 scale

and the idea is to saturate any target area with explosive. Accordingly the MLRS missiles are fired in salvos from a launcher that can hold twelve rockets in two pre-packed containers, each holding six missiles. The containers are loaded into the launchers by a power-loading system and the launchers are carried to the launch position on a tracked chassis based on the American M2 Bradley infantry vehicle but much modified, especially in the suspension area. The MLRS launch vehicle carries a crew of three in a forward-mounted armoured cab and each vehicle contains its own fire control and position reference systems. In addition it has its own crane system to load rocket containers, which also act as launch pods, into the launcher frame. Once loaded the launcher can be traversed and elevated to the correct angle for firing. The rockets may be launched one at a time although they will usually be fired in salvos.

The free-flight ballistic rockets each have a warhead containing 644 fragmentation bomblets, each weighing 0.23 kg. Over the target these bomblets will cover a wide area and each can penetrate up to 100 mm of armour — the effects can be imagined. This type of warhead is not the only one envisaged for one containing 28 AT-2 miniature anti-tank mines is under development in West Germany and another with a self-guiding millimetric radar terminal guidance system is in the early stages of development in the United States.

The problem for the British Army is that this is still all in the future. When MLRS does arrive it will replace the current M107 175 mm long-range guns, and it is anticipated that at least two regiments will be formed.

POLARIS

Body diameter 1.37 m. **Fin span** Not applicable. **Length** 9.7 m. **Weight overall** 16,257 kg. **Weight of warhead** Classified. **Maximum range** 4,600 km. **Minimum range** Not applicable. **Maximum velocity** Classified. **Carrier vehicles** SSBNs — 16 missiles.

The Polaris is an American-designed missile which was procured for the United Kingdom's strategic forces as an independent nuclear deterrent, committed to NATO, as a result of the Nassau Conference in 1962. Originally, five British-built nuclear-powered ballistic missile-carrying submarines (SSBNs) were to be built, but the incoming Labour government amended the procurement to four submarines, the smallest number to keep the deterrent credible by having one at sea at all times.

The 'Resolution' Class SSBNs built for the Royal Navy all carry the Polaris A-3 variant and have similar characteristics to the 'Lafayette' Class SSBNs of the US Navy, being commissioned in 1967 to 1969. To increase the potential of the Polaris A-3 and to give the missiles the ability to penetrate Soviet anti-ballistic missile screens, the Royal Navy was given approval to complete an update programme, known as Chevaline. This work, all carried out in the UK, has been centred on a new warhead system which, although not as independent as the US Multiple Independently-targeted Re-entry Vehicle (MIRV), is nevertheless able to keep the missile credible into the 1990s. At this time, the Trident system should be entering service in new boats.

Polaris is a two-stage missile, with inertial navigation systems which give the exact track to a target, even though 'space' flight is used to bring the missile over the target. On board the 'R' Class submarines, the individual missile is housed in its own launch tube, sixteen of which are situated amidships in the submarine.

Before launch, the missile tube is pressurized to slightly above the local sea water pressure, then high pressure gas is 'squirted' into the bottom of the tube as the casing hatch is opened. The Polaris missile rapidly leaves the tube and as it breaks the surface, the first stage motor ignites to blast the missile clear of the surface and on to its track towards the upper atmosphere.

Aboard the submarine, the procedure for launch is calm and very much like any regular evolution — there is no shout of 'fire' or 'launch'.

Right *For nearly twenty years, the United Kingdom has possessed an independent deterrent force, based around the American-built Polaris missile. Recently, the power of the system has been improved by the Chevaline programme, of British design* (RN).

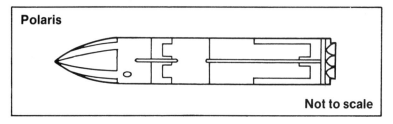

Polaris

Not to scale

The only sensation is the sound of air being pumped into the tube and a slight vibration as the missile leaves the launching tube.

The first-stage motor runs for about one minute to move the missile clear of the ocean surface and away towards the upper atmosphere. This engine is replaced by the second-stage motor, also solid-fuelled, after separation and the missile continues on track for its pre-assigned target. During the flight, powerful inertial guidance systems keep the Polaris on course, controlling the missile's natural tendency to yaw, roll and perhaps even pitch.

At a predetermined point in the trajectory, the second-stage motor shuts off, triggered by the guidance computer and the re-entry module separates at the same time, with the Chevaline warheads on course for a ballistic trajectory directly towards the target. This whole operation takes a matter of minutes.

The targeting of a Polaris missile is a political decision resting with the British Prime Minister of the day and the Polaris boats are under the direct operational control of CINCFLEET (Commander-in-Chief Fleet) from his headquarters at Northwood, north London. There are various special communications systems designed to give him instant assess to the boats on patrol, via very low frequency (VLF) radio transmissions from the radio centre at Rugby and elsewhere on the UK mainland. There are a number of special, secret checks and balances built into the launch sequence, yet the response time is considered adequate to keep Polaris as a credible deterrent.

Polaris will be replaced by Trident some time after 1994.

RAPIER

Body diameter 0.133m. **Fin span** 0.381 m **Length** 2.235 m. **Weight at launch** 42.6 kg. **Maximum range** 6,800 m. **Maximum effective range** 6,500 m. **Minimum range 400 m. Maximum velocity** Mach 2 plus. **Maximum operational height** 3,000 m.

Fire unit weight 1,227 kg. **Fire unit length** 4.064 m. **Fire unit height** 2.134 m. **Fire unit width** 1.778 m. **Radar weight** 1,186 kg. **Radar length** 4.14 m. **Radar height (in action)** 3.378 m. **Radar height (travelling)** 2.032 m. **Radar width** 1.753 m. **Optical tracker weight** 119 kg. **Optical tracker height** 1.549 m. **Tripod diameter** 1.828 m. **Generator weight** 243 kg. **Generator length** 0.991 m. **Generator height** 0.914 m. **Generator width** 0.832 m. **Carrier vehicle** Tracked Rapier — 8 missiles.

Rapier has been one of the major success stories of the British missile industry. It has certainly been one of their most important surface-to-air (SAM) export successes and it has shown itself to be an extremely accurate system as well — the successes during the 1982 Falkland Islands' campaign demonstrated that fact very well.

The Rapier development story can be traced back to the early 1960s when an Army air defence missile known as the PT 428 was first mooted. Early studies disclosed that the PT 428 would be an extremely

Dramatic view of a Rapier just after launching.

Above *A Rapier system deployed in the field with the Blindfire radar unit in the foreground* (Marconi).

Left *A Rapier fire post.*

Above right *Tracked Rapier, which now provides highly mobile low level air defence for the British Army of the Rhine.*

expensive project so in 1962 it was decided to adopt the American Mauler missile system instead. Unfortunately this proved to be a bad choice for it soon transpired that Mauler would be even more expensive, and it was therefore decided to initiate a new British back-up system. The British Aircraft Corporation (now British Aerospace) had been working on a private venture project known as Sightline since 1961 and this formed the basis of the ET.316. The ET.316 system began development in 1963 and the first test firings were made in 1965. This was just as well, for the Americans cancelled their Mauler project in the same year, and in time ET.316 became Rapier. At the time of writing the wheel has turned full circle for with the demise of the DIVADS/Sergeant York mobile gun-based air defence system, the US Army is now actively investigating Rapier as a possible air defence system for its own use.

By 1971 the British Army and Royal Air Force Regiment were receiving their first Rapier systems and they have been active ever since. Those initial deliveries took the form that is still in service, namely a three-part system (or fire post) comprising a fire unit, an optical tracker and a generator, but since those early days the system has been joined by a radar unit. Rapier can operate without the radar but its addition makes the whole system much more flexible and capable of operating under adverse visibility conditions.

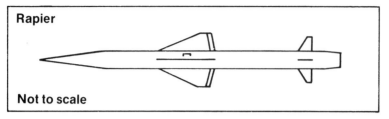

Rapier

Not to scale

A Rapier fire post can be brought into action by a team of seven men. Once in position the complete system covers an area of about 30 m in diameter. The fire post is usually towed into action by two 1-tonne Land Rovers and one 3/4-tonne Land Rover. The first 1-tonne Land Rover tows the fire unit and carries the optical tracker, three men and four missiles. The second 1-tonne Land Rover tows the radar and carries two men and four more missiles. The 3/4-tonne Land Rover carries the other two men, all the stores and more missiles in a special trailer.

Once on the firing site, the fire unit is emplaced and loaded and the optical tracker is set up, plus the radar if required. This radar, known as Blindfire (DN181), then commences a 360° scan out to a range of about 12 km. Any aerial target approaching is automatically interrogated by an IFF (identification friend or foe) signal, and if the result is hostile the operator on the optical tracking unit is alerted. He then searches for the target, as does the fire unit radar head. If both find the target the operator has a choice of either a visual or radar engagment. If radar is selected the sequence is automatic. If a visual engagement is chosen, the operator uses the tracker head and a control joystick to guide the missile. The missile system is so accurate that Rapier has been called a 'hittile' rather than a missile. It is particularly potent when used against low-flying aircraft and helicopters. Each fire unit can cover an area of sky about 100 km^2 in area up to a height of some 3,000 m.

Good as the Rapier system is, it has been the subject of further development. It was appreciated early on in Rapier's service life that it took about fifteen minutes to emplace and that a considerable repair and spares back-up was needed. Rapier is still a rather delicate system to maintain, to the extent that field workshops have to accompany each Rapier unit in the field. However, its main drawback has been a general lack of mobility and for several years the Army was keen to obtain some form of mobile Rapier system. That eventually came about via a rather odd route for British Aerospace also appreciated the mobility problem and had persuaded the late Shah of Iran to purchase a number of Rapier systems built on to modified American M548 tracked cargo carriers. When the Shah fell from power in 1979 this left British Aerospace with a

Tracked Rapier

1:76 scale

57

number of converted vehicles on their hands. Fortunately for them the Army was finally able to obtain funds (during 1981) to purchase these plus some more, and thus the Army obtained Tracked Rapier.

Tracked Rapier is now in service in BAOR. Its advantages over the towed Rapier system are many, not the least of them being the fact that Tracked Rapier can keep up with the armoured formations it is supposed to defend, and is also amphibious. It takes less than fifteen *seconds* to bring into action after a move and its aluminium armour also provides a measure of protection for the crew — towed Rapier crews have virtually no protection other than that they can provide for themselves. Tracked Rapier carries eight missiles on its launcher.

More improvements are in the pipeline. A thermal imaging sight (Darkfire) is a possibility and an entirely new system based on the use of laser rangefinders is in the offing (Laserfire). In the meantime Rapier remains one of the British missile industry's major success stories and seems set fair to remain so for many years.

Tracked Rapier — **Crew** 3. **Weight in action** 14,010 kg. **Length** 6.4 m. **Height, tracker raised** 2.78 m. **Width** 2.8 m. **Track width** 0.381 m. **Ground clearance** 0.41 m. **Maximum road speed** 48 km/h. **Maximum water speed** 5.6 km/h. **Range, roads** 300 km. **Vertical obstacle** 0.609 m. **Maximum gradient** 60 %. **Trench crossing** 1.676 m. **Fording** Amphibious. **Engine** GMC Model 6V-53 6-cylinder diesel developing 210 hp at 2,800 rpm. **Ammunition stowage** 8 missiles on launcher only.

RED TOP

Body diameter 0.222 m. **Fin span** 0.908 m. **Length** 3.27 m. **Weight at launch** 150 kg. **Weight of warhead** 31 kg. **Range** Approx 12 km. **Velocity** Mach 3.2. **Carrier vehicles** Lightning T 5 and F 6 — 2 missiles each.

Red Top is now approaching the end of its service life for when its carrier Lightning interceptors are withdrawn from service as the Tornado F 3s are introduced, the short-range air-to-air Red Tops will be withdrawn also for the Lightnings are the only operational fighter aircraft to have carried them.

The name Red Top was originally a code name that has stuck. The name was bestowed upon the development of a short range infra-red guided missile project that made much use of design and service experience gained from an earlier missile, the Firestreak. At one stage Red Top was even known as Firestreak Mark 4. Red Top carried over many Firestreak features such as the general configuration, but the infra-red guidance system was improved to the point where Red Top could engage aircraft targets from head-on. This was at a time when most infra-red guided missiles were simply 'tail-chasers', as they homed in on their targets' engine exhausts from behind. On Red Top this necessitated a large dome-shaped infra-red sensor head in the nose and some internal re-arrangements such as moving the warhead next to the fuze system. A solid propellant rocket booster motor can propel Red Top to a maximum speed of over Mach 3. Unfortunately, this rocket booster provides Red Top with a range of only approximately 12 km. This is now regarded as far too short for an air-to-air interception missile and for some time Red Top has been regarded as obsolescent. It has remained in service, along with the ageing Lightning interceptors, simply because they were available and for some years there has been nothing to replace them with. That is now changing. With the advent of the Tornado F 3 there is no longer any need to maintain the Lightnings and their Red Tops and they will soon pass from the United Kingdom air defence scene. It will not be before time, for their design and technology dates from the early 1950s.

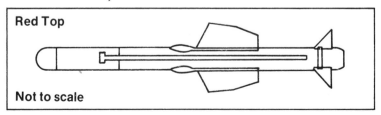

Red Top

Not to scale

Above *Red Top missiles on a Lightning F 6 at RAF Binbrook. Some of the older Firestreaks from which Red Top evolved are still kept at Binbrook for when intercepting Soviet turboprop aircraft such as the Tu-95 Bear, against which they are more effective than Red Top* (MoD).

Below *The Mach 3 Red Top missile now only equips the Lightning air defence squadrons based at RAF Binbrook in Lincolnshire. The missile will be phased out with the Lightning before the end of the decade, but in the meantime it is a valuable air defence weapon* (Brian Service).

ROCKET 66mm HEAT L1A1

Body diameter (calibre) 0.066 m. **Length extended** 0.893 m. **Length closed** 0.655 m. **Length of rocket** 0.508 m. **Weight complete** 2.37 kg. **Weight of rocket** 1 kg. **Max effective range** 300 m. **Armour penetration** Up to 300 mm steel plate. **Muzzle velocity** 145 m/s.

This rocket launcher is not strictly speaking a guided weapon system but it is still an important anti-tank weapon for the British Armed Forces and it does use a rocket to carry its anti-tank warhead to its target. It is an American weapon, known to the US Army as the M72A1 or M72A2, but the British Army know it as the Rocket 66 mm HEAT L1A1 and uses it in considerable numbers. The British Army weapons are not American in manufacturing origin but have been license-produced by Raufoss in Norway. The L1A1 is also used by the Royal Marines and the Royal Air Force Regiment.

The basic design of this anti-tank rocket can be traced back to the days of the German Panzerfaust during World War 2. That was essentially a very close-quarter anti-tank weapon of considerable lethality, and the L1A1 is not too far removed from its original concept. The L1A1 is essentially a simple smooth-bored tube containing a small rocket with a hollow charge warhead which can be very effective against armour. It is light and handy enough to be carried slung over a shoulder, while to save carrying space the tube is carried in a telescoped state and only opened when required for use. Before opening, the waterproof sealing caps at each end of the tube are removed and the weapon is then telescoped out to its full length. This action cocks the percussion firing mechanism and allows the simple sighting system to flip open. The weapon is sighted and fired by pressing a button, with the tube over the firer's shoulder; once fired, the empty tube is discarded. Firing the weapon creates a dangerous area behind the tube caused by the fiery exhaust produced as the rocket is ignited, and which can extend up to 25 m.

If the rocket hits a tank, its hollow charge warhead can cause considerable damage and under favourable conditions it can knock out a tank and its unfortunate crew. Having said that, it must also be stated that the L1A1 is now regarded as, at best, obsolescent and overdue for replacement. The main reason for this is the relatively small calibre (66 mm) of the rocket warhead. This is now too small to make much impression on the armour of most of the modern generation of main battle tanks (although it can still have considerable effect on lighter vehicles such as armoured personnel carriers). The other drawback is the relatively short range of the L1A1. Although it has a maximum range of up to 300 m, it is difficult to aim the weapon accurately at such distances and the effective aiming range is much shorter, placing the firer rather too close to his target for comfort.

The US Army has introduced some design improvements to produce the M72A3 but the British Army has decided to leave the small calibre L1A1 concept alone and move on to an entirely new weapon system for use against armour. This is the LAW 80.

SEACAT

Body diameter 0.60 m. **Fin span** 0.65 m. **Length** 2.0 m. **Weight overall** 68 kg. **Weight of warhead** Classified. **Maximum range** 5 km plus. **Minimum range** Approx 500 m. **Maximum velocity** Approx Mach 0.8. **Carrier vehicles** See text.

Although the Seacat was introduced into service in 1962, it is destined to remain viable until the end of the 1990s, such have been the product improvements made by Short Brothers plc and the Royal Navy. The Seacat is a close-range anti-aircraft missile, with good effect against missile targets and a limited anti-ship ability. It is reliable and cost-effective.

The missile is small, with a relatively large high-explosive blast warhead and proximity fuze, which is powered in flight by a two-stage motor giving initial boost and then sustained flight for a range out to about 5,500 m. Using electronic actuator technology, the missile is manoeuvrable enough to engage low-level supersonic targets, especially attack aircraft, as was proved in the Falklands' conflict. In the early 1980s a height control for a sea skimming flight profile was introduced for programmed engagement of sea-skimming missiles, and a series of successful tests were performed by the Royal Navy. The height control facility is incorporated in one of the missile's four guidance wings and has been retrofitted to stockpiled missiles.

The normal launcher holds four rounds, although there is an export version, known as Lightweight Seacat, which holds three rounds. The reloads are manually loaded which cuts down top weight and the need for complex systems in smaller warships. The missile is activated at launch, with no pre-launch system 'warm-up' needed.

There are three engagement systems for Seacat which have been progressively introduced over the years. Visual engagement uses line-of-sight tracking by an operator who manually acquires the target prior to

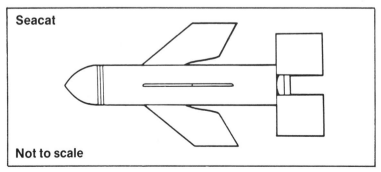

Seacat

Not to scale

Left *The Seacat provided the Royal Navy with its first surface-to-air guided missile defence and now in its third decade, it is still highly effective. The system, seen here launching from a 'Leander' Class frigate, also has the ability to counter surface targets* (Shorts).

Below left *Although the normal RN mounting is four Seacats, Shorts have been highly successful in marketing the three-missile launcher for smaller vessels, such as fast patrol craft* (Shorts).

Right *Drill Seacat rounds mounted in the main deck launcher of a 'County' Class destroyer. Also visible is the missile's director position* (Paul Beaver).

launch. After launch, the missile is manually guided using the fin-mounted flares as a reference.

Seacat Dark Fire was the next improvement which has three sub-options: radar tracking, manual gathering and manual guidance; radar tracking, manual gathering using an electro-optical monitor and manual guidance using the same EO (electro-optical) system; radar tracking, automatic gathering from EO/TV data and the same data collectors providing automatic guidance.

The Blind Fire version of the Seacat engagement system has two sub-options; the first is to use radar tracking, automatic gathering from EO/TV data and manual guidance using a radar display. The second is the use of radar trackers, with automatic gathering and guidance provided by the EO/TV and radar sources respectively.

The Royal Navy currently equips the following classes of warship with Seacat: 'Amazon' Class (Type 21) frigates; 'Ikara Leander' Class (Batch 1) frigates; 'Exocet Leander' Class (Batch 2) frigates; 'Gun Leander' Class (Unmodified Batch 3) frigates; 'County' Class guided missile destroyers; 'Rothesay' Class (Modified Type 12) frigates; *Fearless* and *Intrepid* (assault ships); *Hermes* (aircraft carrier in reserve).

SEA DART

Body diameter 0.42 m. **Fin span** 0.9 m. **Length** 4.36 m. **Weight** at launch 550 kg. **Weight of warhead** Classified. **Maximum range** 30 km plus. **Minimum range** Approx 2 km. **Maximum velocity** Mach 1 plus. **Carrier vehicles** See text.

The Sea Dart, manufactured by British Aerospace, is a dual-role anti-aircraft and anti-ship missile, but it has the primary role of area air defence of the Fleet. It is described as being medium-range, all-weather capable and has been proved in combat during the Falklands' conflict of 1982. Known to the Royal Navy as Guided Weapon System (GWS) 30, Sea Dart has been operational since 1973, having been first brought into service aboard *Bristol*. Subsequently it has equipped all the Type 42 guided missile destroyers and the three light aircraft carriers, *Invincible*,

The Sea Dart missile system provides the basic shipborne defence for the light aircraft carriers of the 'Invincible' Class. The system is designed to provide area air defence and Invincible's *launchers are seen here protected by the blast screen around the launcher* (RN/PO Phot Stewart Kent/Invincible).

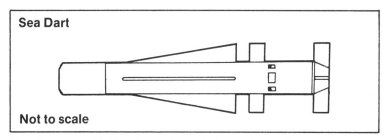

Sea Dart

Not to scale

Illustrious and *Ark Royal*. It will remain in service until at least 2000.

The missile is guided by its own semi-active seeker, with the target illuminated by the continuous wave transmissions of the Type 909 radar from the moment the missile leaves the ship. Using four polyrods (dielectric antennae), the target's orientation can be computed by the missile which then flies a proportional navigation course to intercept the target. With the aid of the four hydraulically powered actuators and the fixed fins to steer, the Sea Dart has considerable manoeuvrability.

In flight, the Sea Dart is powered by an Odin ramjet motor, with initial launch velocity being achieved using the solid-fuel booster, which has its own set of fixed fins. This booster is released on reaching a certain, classified, velocity, allowing the Odin to power the missile to the target which is engaged on a downwards trajectory, if a ship, or by proximity or contact fuze if an aircraft.

Aboard 'Invincible' Class warships, the ship's air and surface search radars detect a target at long range and pass the data to the GWS 30 system. The Type 909 radar acquires the target and the launcher swings towards the target. Once in range, one or two missiles are fired.

When the launcher has been cleared of missiles, it is reloaded rapidly and can be used to ripple fire against a large or combined threat, such as saturation air attack. It is possible for the Sea Dart system to be used against air and surface targets simultaneously; in the past, silver foil-covered balloons have been engaged and hit both at altitude and tethered to the surface using two missiles and near simultaneous launch.

According to the British government White Paper, the Sea Dart achieved eight confirmed kills during the South Atlantic campaign and because the Argentine Navy also fitted Sea Dart to two of its destroyers, it is understood that there was considerable deterrent value in the system. Again according to the White Paper, the 'known capability of the system... forced the Argentine aircraft to fly at low altitude, which made them easier targets for other systems...' It is thought that *Exeter*, a Type 42 destroyer, destroyed a high-flying Lear Jet reconnaissance aircraft

The Sea Dart missile, seen here immediately after launch from a Type 42 destroyer, is initially propelled by a booster motor which takes it away from the ship. For the bulk of the flight, the missile is powered by a Rolls-Royce Odin ramjet (BAe).

over San Carlos Water using Sea Dart and a few days earlier, two A-4 Skyhawks had been destroyed by the same ship's Sea Dart system, east of the Falkland Islands.

The ill-fated *Coventry* is also credited with the destruction of a Pucara strike aircraft over Port Stanley using Sea Dart. The final aircraft loss which the Argentine armed forces suffered in the conflict was again claimed by *Exeter*, the destruction of a night reconnaissance Canberra in the Port Stanley area.

Above *Sea Dart being launched over HMS* Invincible's *Harrier ski-ramp.*

Below *A Sea Eagle just after being released by a Sea Harrier.*

Above *A Lynx helicopter fitted with Sea Skua at RNAS Yeovilton.*

Right *AIM-9L Sidewinders on a Hawk's underwing pylons.*

Below *Sky Flash missiles under the fuselage and Sidewinders under the wings will make a formidable 'fit' for the Tornado F 3; this aircraft is actually the third ADV prototype.*

Swingfire being launched from an FV438.

SEA EAGLE

Body diameter 0.4 m. **Fin span** 1.2 m. **Length** 4.2 m. **Weight at launch** 600 kg. **Weight of warhead** Not released. **Maximum range** 30 km plus. **Minimum range** Approx 500 m. **Maximum velocity** Mach 0.9 plus. **Carrier vehicles** See text.

The British Aerospace Sea Eagle is a medium-weight, long-range, sea skimming anti-ship missile which was designed for fire-and-forget operation against targets at sea. It has been designed for the modern high threat environment and has been 'proofed' against various electronic and decoy counter-measures. It is due to enter service in 1987 with the Royal Navy's Sea Harrier force and the Royal Air Force maritime strike Buccaneer S 2 aircraft. The missile can also be carried by the Tornado GR 1 strike-interdiction aircraft when nominated for an anti-shipping role.

The initial contract for the missile was placed by the UK Ministry of Defence in 1982, at a cost of £200 million. It was successfully test-launched in 1984 and trials were successfully continued in 1985. The missile is capable of sinking or disabling warship targets as large as modern aircraft carriers and the Sea Eagle's software can be re-programmed to overcome new counter-measures or techniques. Using a heavy semi-armour piercing warhead with a special impact-initiated fuze, the missile will penetrate the target before detonation.

Guidance to the Sea Eagle is by active radar homing with the missile seeking head being manufactured by Marconi Space and Defence Systems. It operates in the J-band, using pulse radar techniques to be effective even in severe weather conditions. Targets are usually of 100 m^2 radar cross-section and above.

In flight, the Sea Eagle behaves like an aeroplane, with four cruciform wings mounted almost amidships and with four control fins aft, actuated electrically and controlled by a state-of-the-art microprocessor. The system is described by the manufacturer as all-digital. Sea Eagle is

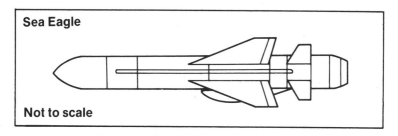

Sea Eagle

Not to scale

Above *Carrying two Sea Eagle anti-shipping missiles, the Sea Harrier FRS 1-mounted system will add greatly to the Royal Navy's over-the-horizon strike capability. Successful trials were first carried out in 1984 and the system will enter service in 1987, probably being taken to sea for the first time in 1988 (BAe).*

Below *A Buccaneer S 2 from A&AEE Boscombe Down demonstrates its ability to carry up to four Sea Eagle missiles for anti-shipping strikes, operating from shore bases. This Buccaneer was flown by a crew from A&AEE, during trials by 31 JSTU which will ensure the system is operational before 1990 (A&AEE/Crown Copyright).*

carried by Sea Harrier aircraft, which need very little additional 'black box' equipment for anti-shipping operations. Two Sea Eagles will normally be carried on NATO standard launchers with special adaptors. Almost any modern high performance aircraft can carry the missile, provided that it has digital weapon management equipment. It is reported that besides Sea Harrier FRS 1/2, Buccaneer S 2, and Tornado GR 1, the Sea Eagle has been cleared for flight on the General Dynamics F-16A/C, McDonnell-Douglas A/F-18 and the British Aerospace Hawk T 1 trainer. In addition, it is thought that the Hawk 200 single-seat lightweight combat aircraft will be adapted to carry the missile on a centre-line pylon, should a customer require it. In addition, a boosted version of the Sea Eagle has been ordered by the Indian Navy for installation on the Westland Advanced Sea King Mk 42B which first flew in August 1985. The missile has been test-fired from the Sea King in hovering and forward flight.

In operation, the Sea Eagle will be given target information by the aircraft's own radar, or on less sophisticated aircraft, by using data linked information, to give the missile target range and bearing data before launch. After launch, the missile uses its own target seeking radar, supplemented by pre-programmed target selection criteria and electronic counter-measures data. The power plant is the Microturbo TRI-60 turbine engine, air breathing and fuelled by kerosene.

The Royal Navy has no firm intention of acquiring the boosted version of the Sea Eagle for its Sea King or EH 101 force, but there is speculation that this situation may change with the lack of flexibility of the current embarked naval aviation caused by the three 'Invincible' Class light aircraft carriers having only two air groups of Sea Harriers and Sea Kings. The missile is very competitively priced compared to the Aerospatiale AM 39 Exocet or the air-launched McDonnell-Douglas Harpoon.

In October 1985, it was confirmed that up to sixty Buccaneer S 2 maritime strike aircraft of the Royal Air Force would be re-worked to carry Sea Eagle, with updated avionics, including the Ferranti FIN 1063 inertial navigation system and Blue Parrot radar.

SEA SKUA (CL 84)

Body diameter 0.25 m. **Fin span** 0.72 m. **Weight at launch** 145 kg. **Weight of warhead** 20 kg. **Maximum range** 15 km plus. **Minimum range** Approx 300 m. **Maximum velocity** Mach 0.8 plus. **Carrier vehicles** See text.

The British Aerospace Sea Skua is a lightweight, all-weather helicopter-launch missile which was designed to operate in conjunction with the Ferranti Sea Spray radar of the Westland Navy Lynx. It entered front-line service with the Royal Navy's Fleet Air Arm in 1982 and was proved in combat in the Falklands' conflict when fired from Lynx HAS 2 helicopters of 815 Squadron. It is reported that the Sea Skua was an outstanding success in the South Atlantic where it was used operationally for the first time, before in fact it had been accepted into full service with the Royal Navy. In all, eight missiles were fired and eight hits reported, which resulted in the sinking of a patrol ship while several other naval targets were so badly damaged that they were forced to retire from the conflict. Thus, the Sea Skua was the first helicopter-launched anti-ship missile to sink a ship in combat.

It is a cost-effective missile which provides the Royal Navy with an over-the-horizon potential, especially against warship targets of less than 1,000 tonnes displacement. It can also be used against larger warships and would inflict severe to disabling damage.

Control and guidance of the Sea Skua is by means of a semi-active radar head, operating in the I-band, with the target illuminated by the Sea Spray radar in the case of the Lynx, although BAe have designed the system to be compatible with several types including the MEL Sea/Super Searcher series. The missile is launched from the helicopter, drops away before the booster motor ignites and the Sea Skua then begins a sea-skimming approach to its target, guided by the TRT radar-altimeter at one of four pre-selected heights, depending on surface conditions.

Besides the Navy Lynx, the Sea Skua has been certified for

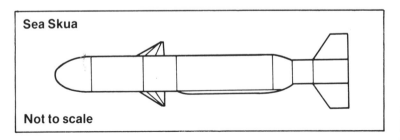

Sea Skua

Not to scale

Above *A surprise introduction to the Falklands conflict was the first operational use of the Sea Skua helicopter-launched anti-shipping missile which is now in full-scale service with the Fleet Air Arm, carried by the Westland Lynx HAS 2 and 3 helicopters. The missile is carried on demountable launchers, with up to four being the standard war load. This picture shows a development Lynx with four trials rounds* (Westland).

Below *The Sea Skua is launched by dropping it from the helicopter, during which time its booster is prepared for firing to take the missile away from the helicopter. Guidance is provided by the helicopter's onboard radar, in this case, the Ferranti Sea Spray Mk1. The missile has been ordered by several nations, including the Federal German government, whose naval Sea King helicopters will carry four on special fuselage-side launchers* (BAe).

The ship-launched variant of the Sea Skua is proposed by British Aerospace to attack targets up to corvette size and could even be fitted to hovercraft and other surface effect cushion craft (BAe).

operational use on the Westland and Agusta Sea King, the EH 101 (which will become operational in 1990/91), Bell 214ST, Bell 412, Agusta-Bell 212, Sikorsky H-76 Eagle and S-70B Seahawk as well as the Kaman SH-2 Seasprite. It is understood that, besides the Royal Navy, Sea Skua has been ordered for service with the Federal German Navy (Sea King update programme), the Turkish Navy (as part of the AB 212 improvement programme) and for the Brazilian Navy's existing and planned Lynx force.

The normal warload for the Lynx, Eagle and AB 212 is four missiles, with more being lifted by the larger helicopters. The missiles can be ripple-fired from the helicopter, depending upon the type of guidance radar carried. In the official White Paper published by the British Government after the Falklands' conflict, the Sea Skua was described as having 'performed excellently' and British Aerospace have made no major modifications to the missile system.

Aboard ship, the Sea Skua is stored as a round of ammunition, with a shelf life of fifteen years, being kept in the magazine with its fins detached. A special trolley is used to support the missile during ground handling operations. Even in the confined space of a warship's hangar, the missile can be loaded and handled with ease, although in the normal course of events it would be loaded on the flight deck.

In flight, the aerodynamic control surfaces are independently controlled and driven by electric actuators, powered by thermal batteries, whilst the rear fins are fixed. The solid-fuel booster has a short duration and is replaced by the solid-fuel sustainer motor during the sea skimming phase of operations. During flight the target and missile must be continually illuminated by the helicopter's radar.

British Aerospace has developed a small ship version of the Sea Skua missile, known as Sea Skua SL, but no orders have been announced as yet.

SEASLUG

Body diameter 0.41 m. **Fin span** 1.4 m. **Length** 6.0 m. **Weight at launch** 252 kg. **Weight of warhead** 35 kg. **Maximum range** 45 km plus. **Minimum range** Approx 1 km. **Maximum velocity** Approx Mach 0.9. **Carrier vehicles** See text.

The beam-riding Seaslug missile was designed as a first generation missile system for the 'County' Class guided missile destroyers of the Royal Navy, and these ships were designed to carry the system in the stern with a large launcher. The magazine is amidships and the reloads pass via a gallery which runs along the length of the ship. The Seaslug I is now out of service and the Seaslug II, with which *Glamorgan* and *Fife*

The venerable Seaslug launcher, with dummy round in place, seen aboard Fife *during Navy Days at Portsmouth. Note the loading and blast doors in the ship's superstructure, below the flight deck.*

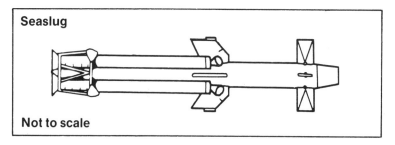

Seaslug

Not to scale

were still armed, was decommissioned in 1985. The missile is also in service with the Chilean Navy.

The Seaslug was designed to engage high-flying targets, such as long-range reconnaissance or bomber aircraft, the latter presumably before they were in position to launch stand-off weapons. The target is acquired by the Type 965 surveillance radar of the 'County' Class guided missile destroyer which passes the information, via the operations room computer, to the Type 901 fire control radar. If the target is to be engaged, the Seaslug launcher can be partially trained and the missile launched by means of four wrap-around boosters which are solid-fuelled.

When the boosters burn out, the missile continues within the radar beam, powered by a sustainer motor which takes the missile to about 45 km and altitudes of about 15,000 m. The boosters are ejected after about five seconds, but in such a way so as not to effect the flight characteristics of the system. Control is performed through cruciform control fins, lined up with cruciform fixed fins to give stability.

The Seaslug missile's warhead is equally effective against surface targets and, during the Falklands' conflict, it is understood that *Glamorgan* fired several salvoes of Seaslug against the Argentine positions at Port Stanley airfield, more for demoralizing the enemy than for an operational reason. Apparently, the telemetry round was fired when it was necessary to reload the launcher with active rounds against possible air attack. The ship's Captain decided to aim the missile in the direction of the airfield and when intelligence reports revealed its effect, it was decided to fire a few rounds each time the ship passed in range on its way to and from the night bombardment positions with its 114 mm gun.

The aerial target is destroyed by the high explosive warhead using either a delayed-action, proximity or contact fuze. The charge is enough to destroy almost all aerial targets.

SEAWOLF

Body diameter 0.18 m. **Fin span** 0.7 m. **Length** 2.0 m. **Weight at launch** 80 kg. **Weight of warhead** Classified. **Maximum range** Approx 10 km. **Minimum range** Approx 300 m. **Maximum velocity** Approx Mach 2 **Carrier vehicles** See text.

The Seawolf is a rapid-response, all-weather naval surface-to-air point-defence weapon system, which has equal abilities against missile and aircraft targets. In trials, the missile even intercepted a 114 mm shell fired from a naval gun. The system was originally designed for the Royal Navy, where it is known as the Guided Weapon System (GWS) 25, and was 'combat proven' in the South Atlantic in 1982, when it is credited with the destruction of five Argentine aircraft.

The warhead is of a blast type, which can be detonated by a proximity fuze or on impact, and is effective against targets at low level or at high

The vertical launch Seawolf has been specified for the Type 23 frigates which will be operational in the 1990s. In addition, there have been plans drawn up for the Type 21 frigates to be fitted with the system in place of the Mk 8 gun and Exocet launchers, but funds will probably not be available (BAe).

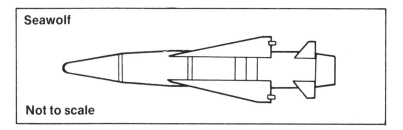

Seawolf

Not to scale

elevation angles, perhaps carrying out a plunging attack. In flight, the missile is guided by aft control fins, moved by a gas-generated actuator commanded by instructions from a radar-line-of-sight system. There are also fixed cruciform wings on the missile's body centre. The system is powered by a solid-fuel motor and the missile can coast to its target after the rocket motor has burned out.

As a rapid response missile system, Seawolf is ideal for smaller warships of the frigate type, especially if those warships are on picket or screen duties. The Royal Navy first installed the Seawolf in the Type 22 or 'Broadsword' Class, using six-missile launchers and later, during refits, five 'Broad Beam Leanders' were fitted with the missile in place of the Seacat. The original plan to fit the Type 21 'Amazon' Class frigates with Seawolf has been scrapped on funding grounds and because the Seacat is still effective in the roles for which the Type 21 will be used.

An idea of the Seawolf's rapid response can be judged by the fact that, in 1982, a flight of four Argentine A-4 Skyhawk strike fighters were attacking the British warships laying off the north coast of the Falkland Islands, when Seawolf was engaged. Two of the four aircraft were destroyed, a third crashed trying to avoid a missile and the fourth abandoned his strike and retired. Sadly, the Seawolf defences had a safety feature to prevent launch if a target of certain size and speed, possibly friendly, crosses the system — this appears to have been the case with *Coventry*, when the attacking aircraft which sank the destroyer were not engaged by Seawolf from a Type 22 because the destroyer had entered the missile engagement zone, manoeuvring to avoid the attacking fighter-bombers.

The missile engages a target when the Type 967/968 surveillance radar of the parent ship detects and then identifies a threat. A computer and the missile system operator evaluate the threat, and if it is to be engaged, the data is passed to Type 910 Seawolf target radar. The Type 910 works directly with the Seawolf system and is an integral part of the GWS 25. Both tracker and launcher train on to the threat's heading, with the tracking radar searching for and then acquiring the target. The tracker locks-on a radar line-of-sight to the target and the missile is launched when in range. After launch, and as the missile approaches and passes supersonic speed, the radar gathers the missile into a tracking beam. The radar watches the missile's flight path and the weapon guidance computer in the ship generates commands to the missile to bring it on track to intercept the target, using a microwave link. Two missiles can be controlled at any one time, both having independent flight paths to the same target, but within the radar beam.

British Aerospace's Naval Weapons Division has received a contract, worth £130 million from the UK Ministry of Defence to prepare the vertical-launch Seawolf for the future Type 23 frigate programme. In August 1985, the two-stage VL Seawolf was successfully launched and separated without disturbing the missile's flight path. It is a lightweight system which uses the basic Seawolf missile, with a tandemly arranged booster and sustainer motors. Being vertical launch, the system eliminates blind arcs of fire from the ship, increases the effective interception range of the Seawolf and enables the weapon to be used to defeat saturation air and missile attacks. The system will come into operational use with the first 'Duke' Class.

A third variant of the seawolf is the Lightweight Seawolf system which is suitable for warships down to 900 tonnes and which uses light-weight tracking radars. The UK Ministry of Defence has selected the Marconi ST 085SW radar for the Royal Navy's Type 22 frigate refit programme; the radar eliminates multipath returns and other surface clutter which affect the tracking accuracy of the system against low-level targets. The launcher is four-missile in capacity.

Left *The trials Seawolf launcher, mounted on the flight deck of* Penelope, *a 'Leander' Class frigate, during the 1970s. The launcher is relatively lightweight and, although re-supplied manually, is highly effective in action* (RN/PO Phot Smart).

Above right *Loading the Seawolf missile, which can be treated as a round of ammunition aboard ship, into the trials launcher of* Penelope (RN/PO Phot Smart).

Right *Seawolf away! The missile is launched through clam-shell protective doors* (RN).

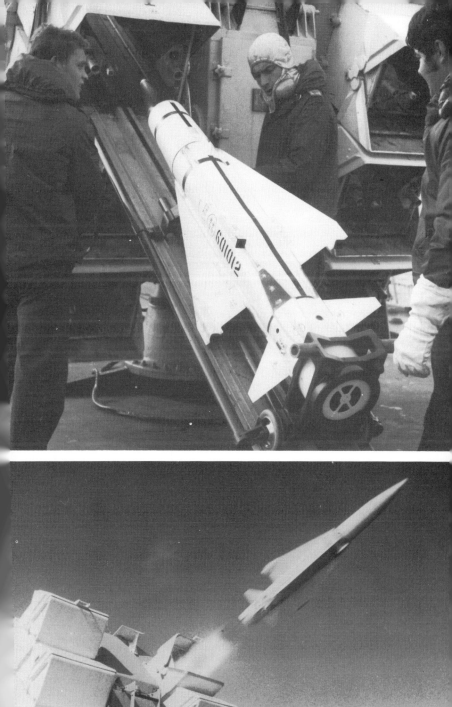

SHRIKE

Body diameter 0.2 m. **Fin span** 0.914 m. **Length** 3.048 m. **Weight** 177 kg. **Weight of warhead** 66 kg. **Range** Estimated 12 to 16 km. **Velocity** Mach 2.

The Shrike anti-radiation missile entered the United Kingdom's missile arsenal under unusual circumstances. For many years the Royal Air Force had lacked a guided missile that could home in on the radiation transmitted by enemy radars and destroy them. This ommission was highlighted during the 1982 Falkland Islands' campaign and in a remarkably short time a number of Shrike missiles were procured direct from the United States. They were then carried by Vulcan B 2 bombers during their long range 'Black Buck' missions against the Argentinian defences on the islands and proved to be highly effective weapons.

Anti-radiation missiles such as the Shrike can have two effects upon an enemy. If he does not realise that anti-radiation missiles are being used against him then his radars will be destroyed. If he does suspect something like Shrike is likely to be used the simplest protection is to simply switch off the radars. This fools the missile but renders the enemy blind to what is going on around him which can be just as effective as knocking out the radar in the first place.

Shrike missiles actually seen here fitted to a US Marine Corps JA-4M Skyhawk (US Navy).

The Shrike is known to the American armed forces as the AGM-45A. Operationally it is carried by an aircraft with radiation sensors that can pick up enemy radar signals to alert the missile operator. He switches on the radar-seeker head in the missile and this allows the Shrike to obtain a 'fix' on the source. When the carrier aircraft is in range the missile is launched and then flies on to its target under the control of the seeker head. Once on target the large high-explosive fragmentation warhead can be virtually guaranteed to knock out the offending radar installation.

The American armed forces have a number of special seeker heads to cover the large number of frequency bands that might be used. At least thirteen of these special heads are available to the American armed forces but which or how many of them are in use with the Royal Air Force is not known, or ever likely to be disclosed. It is also not known what types of Royal Air Force aircraft can now carry the Shrike as the carrier used so effectively during the Falklands' campaign was the Vulcan B 2, an aircraft that has now passed from service. However, it seems extremely unlikely that the Royal Air Force, having found the Shrike so useful in one campaign, will simply drop the missile from its inventory. The Nimrod maritime reconnaissance aircraft crews would no doubt find many tactical excuses to carry a Shrike on their long-range missions and no doubt there are many other potential carrier aircraft.

So determined is the Royal Air Force to retain an anti-radar missile in its armoury that the development of an entirely new and all-British anti-radiation weapon is now under way. This missile is known as ALARM (qv) (Air-Launched Anti-Radar Missile) and is scheduled to enter service from 1987 onwards. When it does enter service it will be used mainly by the Tornado squadrons to knock out enemy defence and weapon system control radars during their interdiction and deep strike missions.

SIDEWINDER AIM-9

Body diameter 0.13 m. **Fin span** 0.6 m. **Length** 2.87 m. **Weight at launch** 85 kg. **Weight of warhead** 3 kg. **Maximum range** 5 km plus. **Minimum range** 500 m. **Maximum velocity** Mach 2 plus. **Carrier vehicles** See text.

The British forces use the AIM-9L version of the highly successful Raytheon Sidewinder missile, which was first developed for the US Air Force in the 1950s. The AIM-9L proved highly successful in the Falklands' conflict and, according to the official British government White Paper, the Sea Harriers of the Royal Navy scored sixteen confirmed 'kills' and one probable with the missile.

The AIM-9L is the third generation of the Sidewinder with an all-aspect infra-red homing and seeking head which gives the system dogfight capability. The missile is reported to use a highly advanced active optical laser fuze and special fragmentation devices for proximity as well as contact detonation. In-flight correction to the trajectory is carried out by electric actuators powering the notched delta fins just behind the aiming head, whilst the large fins aft are fixed.

The European version of the AIM-9L, which will now be delivered to the British forces, is made by a consortium of Federal Germany, Norway, Italy and the United Kingdom, led by Bodenseewerk Geratetechnik, with British Aerospace supplying components for the programme.

Besides the Sea Harrier FRS 1 (and planned mountings on the Sea

The AIM-9L Sidewinder was one of the great success stories of the South Atlantic campaign - another was the Sea Harrier FRS 1 naval fighter. After the conflict, all Fleet Air Arm Sea Harriers were fitted for carrying four Sidewinders, rather than the previous warload of two. In this picture, two aircraft from 899 Squadron show the four Sidewinder fit, plus the ASW (Acquisition Sidewinder) loads for air-to-air fighter training (BAe).

Above *Another user of the Sidewinder in the South Atlantic were the Nimrod long-range maritime reconnaissance aircraft, which were engaged in sorties from Ascension island, often close to the Argentine coastline and within range of air defence fighters* (Bob Downey).

Below *Four Sidewinders about to be loaded on to a Phantom FGR 2 at RAF Coningsby* (MoD).

Part of the war load of the Tornado F 2 / 3, the Sidewinder will be replaced in due course by the ASRAAM, but until about 1990, the AIM-9 will remain the dogfight or close-range missile for air defenders of the United Kingdom. The Sidewinder is loaded on the wing pylons in this picture – on the fuselage racks are Sky Flash missiles (BAe).

Harrier FRS 2), the AIM-9L is carried on most of the combat aircraft of the Royal Air Force. The principal users are the air defence aircraft — the Phantom FG 1, Phantom FGR 2, Phantom F-4J and Tornado F 3. In addition, the missile is used for self-defence by the Jaguar GR 1, Harrier GR 3 (and planned for the Harrier GR 5), the Buccaneer S 2, Nimrod MR 2, Tornado GR 1 and by the Hawk T 1 in the airfield defence role.

The Harrier GR 3 strike aircraft which were deployed to the Falkland Islands in 1982 were modified to take Sidewinder in about a week and the aircraft now retain the ability to be armed with the missile. The Nimrod long-range maritime reconnaissance force operating from Ascension Island was similarly converted to provide self-defence against Argentine Air Force and Naval Air Arm fighters. The RAF has since been allocated funds to convert all 34 Nimrod MR 2 aircraft to carry Sidewinder. In addition, funds have been made available to stockpile Sidewinder (and other missiles) for future Out of Area conflicts so as not to affect NATO war stocks and planning.

A suggestion to arm the RAF's medium support helicopters with Sidewinder has not been progressed, but there is considerable general interest in the AIM-9M version of the Sidewinder, which can be used in a more hostile ECM and decoy environment. The missile will be replaced in the 1990s with ASRAAM.

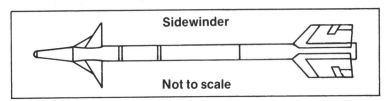

Sidewinder

Not to scale

SKY FLASH

Body diameter 0.203 m. **Fin span** 1.02 m. **Length** 3.7 m. **Weight** 192 kg. **Weight of warhead** 30 kg. **Range** 40 km. **Velocity** Mach 4. **Carrier vehicles** Tornado F 3, Phantom FGR 2 — 4 missiles each.

Originally known as Project XJ521, Sky Flash began life in 1973 with initial trials being completed in 1977. A production contract followed and the missile is now in service not only with the Royal Air Force but also with the Swedish Air Force. The basis of the Sky Flash 'airframe' is the American Raytheon Sparrow, but it is equipped with an entirely British electronics suite. The prime contractor is the British Aerospace Dynamics Group with Marconi responsible for the homing system and Thorn EMI producing the important radar proximity fuze. Raytheon still act as an important sub-contractor.

Sky Flash is a semi-active, medium-range, air-to-air guided missile capable of attacking a wide range of aircraft targets from very low to

The first prototype Tornado F 2 is shown carrying the new Sky Flash missile on fuselage pylons and the Sidewinder missile on wing racks, adjacent to the long range fuel tanks. Tornado has been described as the best air defence aircraft available in the mid-1980s and the armament it carries is certainly state-of-the-art (BAe).

During trials with the Sky Flash air-to-air missile, this Tornado F 2 (Air Defence Variant) is shown during a test flight from the British Aerospace facility at Warton, on the Irish Sea coast of Lancashire (BAe).

extremely high altitudes and in all weathers. The homing radar employs what are known as monopulse techniques to bestow a very high degree of resistance to enemy electronic counter-measures (ECM). The radar system also has what is known as a 'snap up' facility that allows the missile to be launched from altitudes as low as 100 m — at high altitudes

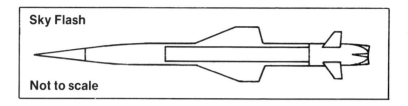

Sky Flash

Not to scale

the same facility can be used for 'snap down' engagements of aircraft targets flying as low as 75 m, even against the usual clutter of ground-produced radar returns. Several other British innovations have been introduced on Sky Flash, most of them based on the use of solid-state electronics, and including the autopilot together with the power systems (including thermal batteries). British Aerospace manufactures the missile structure and carries out final assembly and testing.

The first Royal Air Force fighter to be equipped with the Sky Flash was the Phantom FGR 2 which can carry four missiles. The new Tornado F 3 air defence variant (ADV) also carries four missiles. On each of these interceptors the missiles are carried under the fuselage in recesses to reduce their drag as much as possible. On the Phantom the Sky Flash supplements Sparrow missiles — on the Tornado F 3 only Sky Flash will apparently be used with a specially developed release system that allows the missiles to be fired throughout the Tornado's considerable flight envelope.

SPARROW

Body diameter 0.2 m. **Fin span** 1.02 m. **Length** 3.66 m. **Weight** 227 kg. **Weight of warhead** 40 kg. **Range** 40 km plus. **Velocity** Mach 3.5. **Carrier vehicles** Phantom FG Mark 1 and FGR Mark 2 — up to 4 missiles each.

The Sparrow is an American missile that was virtually accepted as part and parcel of the Phantoms when they were purchased by the British Armed Forces back in the mid-1960s. It is described as a medium-range, all-weather air-to-air guided missile known to the Americans as the AIM-7. Both the US Air Force and US Navy use a number of versions but that used by the Royal Air Force is the AIM-7F.

The AIM-7F Sparrow is produced by the Raytheon Company of Bedford, Massachusetts. It has a semi-active radar homing head and can be fitted with either a contact or a proximity fuze. The guidance system can deal with targets flying at all altitudes from sea level to 'very high' and uses solid-state electronics that enable the missile to engage a target after a time-from-start (including launch) as short as two seconds.

The Sparrow is now being replaced by the Sky Flash (a missile that is basically a Sparrow with a new electronics suite) in the Royal Air Force Phantom squadrons and it appears that it will not be used on the new Tornado F 3. In the United States, development of the Sparrow continues. The Americans now have a version with an improved overall performance capability similar to the British Sky Flash and the basic Sparrow design has proved so adaptable that it is now being used on US Navy vessels as a surface-to-air defence missile. Thus, although the Royal Air Force will gradually phase out the Sparrow, the Americans will continue to use it for years to come.

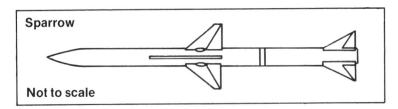

Sparrow

Not to scale

Above right *Sparrow missiles being loaded on to an RAF Phantom* (MoD).

Right *Another Sparrow being fitted to a similar aircraft* (RAF).

SUB-HARPOON

Data as for Harpoon. Capsule body diameter 0.53 m. **Length** 6.25 m. **Weight overall** 325 kg.

The Sub-Harpoon is an American-designed submarine-launched missile system which permits a submarine to strike at long-range against surface targets without the need to close-in, through a protective screen of escorts, for torpedo operations. The Royal Navy's interest followed a development programme by the US Navy which began in 1972, and by 1979/80, the submarine *Churchill* had carried out an eight months' series of trials off the American coast, using the US Navy's range facilities. In the trials, *Churchill* fired more than 120 capsules, including completely live missiles against ship targets.

The missile, which is launched in encapsuled form through the submarine's torpedo tubes, is stored in the weapons compartment of modern nuclear-powered submarines (SSNs) and supplements the existing Tigerfish and the future Spearfish torpedo systems. In Royal Naval service, the Sub-Harpoon is known as UGM-84B.

The missile is pre-programmed prior to launch, and the guidance system is backed up by active homing (with electronic counter-counter measures), plus terminal manoeuvring systems. The data processor on board receives both targeting and altitude data before launch and knows the general direction to follow after breaking the surface, directional information being fed to the four manoeuvring fins on the missile's body. After launch from the torpedo tube by means of compressed air release, the booster motor ignites to take the missile clear of the submarine and through the surface to the air. The air-breathing sustainer motor then takes over for the cruise at sea-skimming height towards the target.

In the approximate target area, the active homing head comes on, defeats ship's jamming, having used mid-course guidance from various sources, including the parent submarine or friendly aircraft operating in concert with the submarine. It is now thought that all the 'Trafalgar', 'Swiftsure' and 'Churchill' Class submarines are equipped with Sub-Harpoon and it is possible that the R-Class nuclear-powered ballistic missile submarines — 'bomber' boats —have the system.

SWINGFIRE

Body diameter 0.17 m. **Fin span** 0.373 m. **Length** 1.067 m. **Weight at launch** 37 kg. **Maximum range** 4,000 m. **Minimum range, direct fire** 150 m. **Minimum range, separated** 300 m. **Arc of fire, traverse** 90°. **Arc of fire, elevation** —10° to +20°. **Velocity** Subsonic. **Armour penetration** Not released. **Carrier vehicles** FV438 — 2 missiles or FV102 Striker — 4 missiles.

Swingfire has been around for some time. It can trace its origins back to the late 1950s when it was a Fairey missile project with the code name 'Orange William', and when Fairey came under the British Aircraft Corporation (later British Aerospace) umbrella during one of the many mergers and take-overs of the period it became Swingfire. By 1969 it had been accepted by the British Army for the long range anti-tank guided weapon (LRATGW) role which it has retained ever since.

Despite its long service life, Swingfire is still a very potent anti-tank guided missile. its large warhead means that it can tackle virtually any tank it might encounter and come off best and its chances of doing so are still high, even on the electronic battlefields of today. Its virtually immunity from the sort of jamming many more modern missile guidance systems might suffer is due to the fact that Swingfire still uses a wire

A Swingfire being launched from one of the four missile bins on the rear of an Army Striker vehicle.

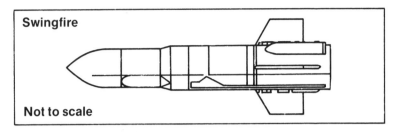

Swingfire

Not to scale

guidance system and a form of optical guidance that is virtually foolproof.

Swingfire missiles are issued in sealed containers and are treated as normal pieces of ammunition. They are fired from one of two vehicles, the FV438 or the FV102 Striker. The FV438 is a member of the FV432 armoured personnel carrier family with two roof-mounted launchers that can be reloaded from within the vehicle. The FV102 Striker has four roof-mounted launchers that have to be reloaded from outside. Both vehicles have a roof-mounted sighting system, but their crews can also use sights which may be located (or separated) some distance away from the launch vehicle to make best use of cover or for other tactical reasons. A thermal imaging sight for use at night or in poor visibility is also available.

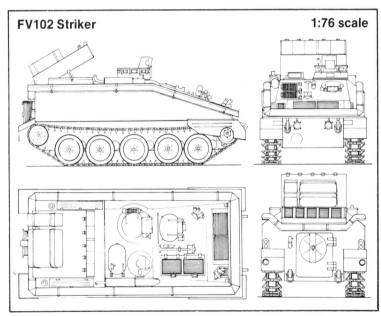

FV102 Striker　　　　　　　　　　　　　　　　**1:76 scale**

Front view of a Striker with its Swingfire missile bins raised.

After launch the Swingfire missile is pre-programmed to fly into the centre of the line-of-sight of the sight in use — it is this ability to make a rapid flight correction soon after launch that gives the Swingfire missile its name, since the sight can be at a considerable angle from the launch angle. In flight the missile is controlled by the operator's thumb joystick on the sight unit. On most occasions the guidance changes need only be minor for the angle of the sight from the angle of launch is computed constantly with corrections being passed through the guidance wires. The Swingfire missile flies at a relatively leisurely pace compared with other missile systems so corrections are usually fairly easy to make and are introduced to offset side wind influences and other such factors.

For many years Swingfire was a province of the Royal Artillery but the LRATGW role has now been passed to the Royal Armoured Corps. The FV102 Strikers operate today with the armoured reconnaissance regiments and the FV438s operate with the armoured regiments. There is a considerable logistic and technical back-up organization for Swingfire as well as a number of ongoing training systems, including one that is incorporated into the Swingfire sight — this provides a simulated 'missile' signal into the sight to provide practise with the guidance controls.

TOW

Body diameter 0.152 m. **Fin span** Not released. **Length** 1.168 m. **Weight at launch** Approx 24 kg. **Maximum range** 3,750 m. **Minimum range** 65 m. **Maximum velocity** 200 m/s plus. **Armour penetration (60°)** 408 mm. **Carrier vehicle** Lynx AH 1 and 7 helicopter (up to 8 missiles).

Tow stands for Tube-launched, Optically tracked, Wire-guided which effectively sums up the main features of this missile. TOW is an American anti-tank weapon which was introduced into British Army use following trials held between the British Aerospace Hawkswing (a variant of the Swingfire), the Franco-German HOT and the TOW. TOW emerged successfully and the first entered British Army service during the early 1980s. By then TOW was not a particularly novel missile as the first of them was fired in the United States during 1965. By the 1980s it was already in widespread service with the American forces under the military designation of BGM-71A or M151A2. The main change as far as the British Army was concerned was that, while the American Army TOW was used as a ground-mounted missile system firing from a tripod-mounted or vehicle launcher, the British Army TOWs are fired only from

By 1985, the Lynx AH 1 helicopter, armed with eight Hughes Aircraft TOW anti-tank missiles, using the BAe/Hughes roof-mounted sight, had become one of the most important defences against massed main battle tank assaults on the NATO Central Region. Until the fitting of the night or thermal imager sight, the Lynx/TOW only has a daylight role but BAOR commanders believe that the helicopter has the ability, in massed counter-attacks, to destroy a battalion of tanks in thirty seconds (Westland).

Two effective British Army missile systems in the same picture. The British Army of the Rhine's new Tracked Rapier, said to be one of the best systems in the world in defence against anti-armour helicopters, and a Lynx AH 1, armed with TOW, during exercises.

helicopters. The American forces do make use of helicopter-fired TOWs but the British make no use of the ground-launched versions at all as their TOWs are launched from the Lynx helicopter.

TOW has two rocket motors, one of which fires the missile from its tube and the other provides the main flight propulsion. In flight, TOW is a relatively fast-moving missile and it was this feature that caused the British Army to select it over all others. The rocket motor exhausts through two side-mounted nozzles to allow the back of the missile to be used for the guidance system. As the rocket moves forward two thin

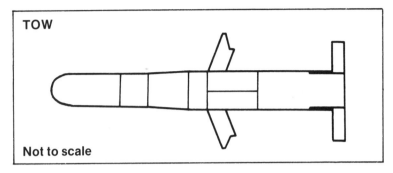

TOW

Not to scale

wires unwind back to the launcher through which flight correction commands are transmitted from the automatic guidance system. The missile gunner keeps the optical sight graticules on the target and the system does the rest.

On the Lynx helicopter a BAe–Hughes roof-mounted sight is used to track the missile in flight and each Lynx can carry up to four TOW missile tubes on each side. Over the years the Army Air Corps has devoted a great deal of thought into methods of using their TOWs to the maximum effect and by now have evolved a number of tactical ploys to surprise and disrupt armoured attacks, called 'Helarm', including working in close co-operation with US Air Force A-10 Thunderbolt IIs with their powerful 30 mm rotary cannon. Most Lynx tactics make great use of all available cover and folds in the ground to allow them to approach their targets undetected. This approach is quickly followed by a rapid missile attack lasting thirty seconds and a hasty retreat to a new location.

Unfortunately, the basic TOW missile has now been rendered less effective by recent increases in Soviet tank armour. The Americans have for some time appreciated that the hollow-charge warhead used on TOW is no longer capable of penetrating the frontal armour of some Soviet tanks and have made some changes to their missiles to overcome this problem. Methods employed include an increased stand-off fuzing system and an even larger warhead. As far as is known none of these improvements have yet to filter through to the British TOWs. Even so, TOW is still a powerful anti-tank weapon more than capable of dealing with the vast bulk of any attacking armour fleet.

TRIDENT

Body diameter 1.88 m. **Fin span** Not applicable. **Length** 10.36 m. **Weight overall** Approx 30,000 kg. **Weight of warhead** Classified. **Maximum range** 7,400 km. **Minimum range** Not applicable. **Maximum velocity** Classified. **Carrier vehicles** See text.

The Trident 2D5 missile, which the UK government has ordered to provide the nuclear deterrent force in the 1990s and beyond, has a three-stage propulsion system, requiring only one nozzle per stage, unlike the early Polaris A-3 currently in service. The missile is propelled by solid-fuel and is guided by a complex inertial navigation system which is understood to be capable of mid-course correction, using data from star-fixes taken en route. The Trident 1C4 became operational with the US Navy in 1979.

Trident, like Polaris, will be entirely under British control, but will be committed to NATO and will be carried in four new-build submarines, each with sixteen tubes, with 32 warheads per missile. The Trident force will be based on the River Clyde at Faslane and the 2D5 missile system, together with the Strategic Weapon System (back-up and command/control) was decided upon in 1984. The Trident-type submarines, to be built by Vickers at Barrow, will be larger than the 'R' Class which carry Polaris, with a scaled-down 'Ohio' Class missile compartment. A large number of British companies are involved in the Trident programme, either as contractors to the British version or in off-set agreements with the US manufacturers.

INDEX